Earth Science 6
Student Guide

Part 1

About K12 Inc.

K12 Inc., a technology-based education company, is the nation's leading provider of proprietary curriculum and online education programs to students in grades K–12. K^{12} provides its curriculum and academic services to online schools, traditional classrooms, blended school programs, and directly to families. K12 Inc. also operates the K^{12} International Academy, an accredited, diploma-granting online private school serving students worldwide. K^{12}'s mission is to provide any child the curriculum and tools to maximize success in life, regardless of geographic, financial, or demographic circumstances. K12 Inc. is accredited by CITA. More information can be found at www.K12.com.

Table of Contents

Student Worksheets and Assessments

Unit 1: Earth's Surface

Unit 2: Rocks and Minerals

Unit 3: Geologic History

Unit 4: Plate Tectonics

Unit 5: Air, Weather, and Climate

Unit 6: Semester 1: Review and Assessment

Student Guide
Lesson 1: Introduction to Earth Science

Every day you feel the ground beneath you, breathe the air around you, and drink water you need to survive. Today you are starting a trip around and into planet Earth. Your trip will include journeys from the Earth's surface deep into its hot core, through its oceans, into its atmosphere, and far beyond to distant planets, stars, and galaxies.

Welcome to Earth Science!

What comes to mind when you think of "Earth"? If you think only about earthquakes and volcanoes or rocks and soil, you are in for a surprise. Earth science involves much more. Earth science deals with everything from the center of the Earth to the matter at the far reaches of the universe. Whether you study fossils or Force 5 tornadoes, you're still doing Earth science. What else is there to learn about Earth? Continue on for a preview of this year's course.

Lesson Objectives

- Explore concepts to be addressed during the year in Earth Science.

PREPARE

Approximate lesson time is 60 minutes.

Materials

For the Student

    📖 Keeping a Science Notebook

    binder, 3-ring

    folders

    hole punch

    tabbed dividers

    paper

LEARN
Activity 1: Welcome to Earth Science *(Online)*

Activity 2: Keeping a Science Notebook *(Offline)*

Get ready for an exciting experience as you begin this semester of Earth Science. One thing you will need this year is a **Science Notebook**. This is more than just a place to stash your papers and jot down definitions. In your Science Notebook, you can take notes as you read through the Explore sections in online lessons. Store lesson review sheets, lab notes, and activity notes in your notebook. Let's find out how to organize a good Science Notebook. You may want to read this activity with an adult who can help you find supplies.

Name _____   Date _____

Keeping a Science Notebook

The Notebook

Have an adult help you find the following supplies to make an organized Science Notebook:

- 3-ring binder

- hole punch

- tabbed dividers

- loose-leaf paper

- folders with holes for a 3-ring binder (for projects or papers you don't want to hole-punch)

The Sections

Use a pencil to write the names of each unit on your tabbed dividers. If you do not have enough room on the tabs, you can shorten their titles. The units are:

- Earth's Surface

- Rocks and Minerals

- Geologic History

- Plate Tectonics

- Air, Weather, and Climate

- Water on Earth

- Energy and Earth's Resources

- Our Place in the Universe

- Scientific Investigation

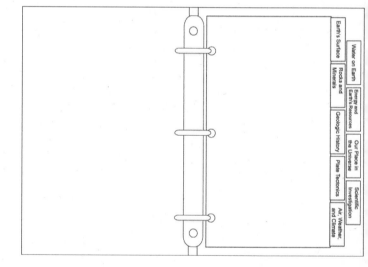

The Papers

Let's review the types of papers you will store in your notebook.

- **Lesson activity sheets:** During activities, you may have to make observations or collect data, draw figures, or answer questions on activity sheets.

- **Lesson review sheets:** Almost every lesson contains a lesson review sheet to help you remember the new words and information you learned in the lesson.

- **Lesson notes:** You will practice note-taking skills at times during the year by writing down important information as you read the lessons.

- **Lesson assessments:** You may need to take some assessments on paper.

- **Lab notes:** A few times during the course, you will complete labs. During these lessons, you will have to take careful notes and make observations.

- **Other papers:** You may want to keep drawings, notes, articles, or other science-related information in your notebook.

The Directions

In each lesson, look for directions to store papers in your Science Notebook. Place each one behind the papers you have already stored.

Now, once you have organized your notebook, place this sheet in the first section, behind the first tab.

Student Guide
Lesson 2: Spheres of the Earth

Scientists like to work with definitions. It helps them make sense of the complicated world we live in. Earth scientists talk about layers or spheres as a way to describe how complex the earth is. Understanding these spheres and how they interact makes earth science easier to comprehend.

Lesson Objectives

- Describe features of the layers, or spheres, that make up the earth system (atmosphere, biosphere, lithosphere, hydrosphere, and magnetosphere).
- Explain that the earth is made up of layers (internally and on the surface).
- Define the biosphere as the zone of life on Earth that includes all living things.

PREPARE

Approximate lesson time is 60 minutes.

Materials

For the Student

- Which Sphere?
- Spheres of the Earth Lesson Review

Keywords and Pronunciation

atmosphere : the gaseous layer surrounding the earth, made up of the mixture of substances known as air; the earth´s atmosphere is made up of many gases, including the oxygen we need to breathe, as well as small liquid and solid particles

aurora : streamers or bands of light sometimes visible in the night sky in northern or southern regions of the earth; scientists think an aurora is caused by charged particles from the sun that enter the earth´s magnetic field and stimulate molecules in the atmosphere

biosphere (BIY-uh-sfir) : the zone of life on the earth that includes all living things; plants, fungi, and animals are all parts of the earth´s biosphere

hydrosphere (HIY-druh-sfir) : the liquid layer of the earth, made up of the earth´s waters; the oceanic parts of the hydrosphere cover about three-fourths of the earth´s surface

lithosphere (LIH-the-sfir) : the rocky outer layer of the solid earth, averaging about 100 km in depth; the lithosphere includes the continents, islands, and the entire ocean floor

magnetosphere (mag-NEE-tuh-sfir) : the region in space that is affected by the earth´s magnetic field; solar wind and other particles in space are deflected by the earth´s magnetosphere

LEARN
Activity 1: More than Meets the Eye *(Online)*

Activity 2: Which Sphere? *(Offline)*
What's going on in earth's spheres? Decide which spheres are involved in events that occur each day on earth.

Activity 3: Spheres of the Earth *(Offline)*
Review what you have learned about the earth's spheres. When finished, place your completed lesson review sheet in your Science Notebook.

ASSESS
Lesson Assessment: Spheres of the Earth (*Online*)
You will complete an online assessment covering the main objectives of this lesson. Your assessment will be scored by the computer.

Name _____   Date _____

Which Sphere?

Anything that happens on earth occurs within one or more of earth's spheres. Below you will find several statements describing events that take place every day.

Identify which sphere(s) are involved in each event. Label each statement with a **H, B, A, L**, and/or **M** indicating that it takes place in either the *hydrosphere, biosphere, atmosphere, lithosphere, or magnetosphere.* You may use some letters more than once, and some statements may describe events that occur in more than one sphere simultaneously.

_____1. Bees pollinating flowers

_____2. Desert sand blowing across the dunes

_____3. A farmer plowing the earth to plant crops

_____4. Clouds floating in the sky

_____5. Water flowing in a river

_____6. Fish swimming in the ocean

_____7. The earth being protected from charged particles

_____8. Snow on the Rocky Mountains

_____9. A foggy day

_____10. Waves pounding and shaping cliffs

Describe the Sphere

Now it is your turn to observe the world around you and describe the ways in which the spheres of the earth work together to shape our beautiful planet. Create a one-sentence statement to illustrate the interaction of the following spheres.

11. The lithosphere and the biosphere

_____

_____

12. The atmosphere and the hydrosphere

_____

_____

13. The biosphere and the hydrosphere

_____

_____

14. The atmosphere and the biosphere

_____

_____

15. The lithosphere, hydrosphere, and biosphere

_____

_____

16. The atmosphere, lithosphere, and hydrosphere

_____

_____

Name _____   Date _____

Spheres of the Earth Lesson Review

Review what you have learned about earth's spheres. When finished, place your completed lesson review sheet in your Science Notebook.

Making an Outline

Taking notes in an outline helps you organize information that has many parts. Broad subjects make up the major headings, and details are underneath. Roman numerals and letters are used to organize them.

Read the Explore section of your lesson and fill in the blanks in the outline below.

Earth's Spheres

1. **Biosphere**

    a. contains all life on earth

    b. examples: plants, animals, fungi

2. **Hydrosphere**

    a. contains all water on earth

    b. examples: oceans, _____

3. _____

    a. rocky outer layer of solid earth

    b. examples: _____

4. **Atmosphere**

    a. contains: _____

    b. _____

5. _____

    a. _____

    b. example: auroras, where charged particles are trapped

Student Guide
Lesson 3: Mapping the Earth

Our modern maps are more detailed and precise than those of early explorers. How did early explorers make their maps? They kept careful records of landforms (hills, valleys, bodies of water, and so on), the position of the sun, even the motion of the sea. Today, satellites in orbit around the earth do most of the work of mapmaking. But even now, mapmaking is tricky. Mapmakers must take a round object and represent it on a flat surface.

Lesson Objectives

- Interpret maps using scale, directional indicators, keys, and symbols to locate physical features.
- Use latitude and longitude to locate places on a map.
- Determine the scale of a map.

PREPARE

Approximate lesson time is 60 minutes.

Advance Preparation

- If you don't already have it, you will need to gather dried beans or peas.

Materials

For the Student

    📖 Ring of Fire

    beans, dry - (or dried peas)

    K12 Wall Map

    📖 Mapping the Earth Lesson Review

Keywords and Pronunciation

cartographer (kahr-TAH-gruh-fuhr) : a person who makes maps

latitude (LA-tuh-tood) : a distance in degrees north and south of the equator

longitude (LAHN-juh-tood) : a particular distance east or west of the prime meridian running through Greenwich, England, measured as an angle at the earth´s center and expressed in degrees; lines of longitude meet at the poles

map legend : a section of a map that explains the meanings of symbols and that may contain the map scale; symbols for airports, recreation areas, campsites, and other areas of interest may appear in a map legend

map projection : a way to transfer information from a three-dimensional curved surface to a two-dimensional medium, such as paper or a computer screen

meridians : lines of longitude that run vertically from the north pole to the south pole; meridians terminate at the poles

prime meridian (priym muh-RIH-dee-uhn) : the imaginary vertical line, running north to south, from which longitude is measured; the prime meridian runs right through England

LEARN

Activity 1: Round Earth, Flat Map *(Online)*

Activity 2: Ring of Fire *(Online)*

Activity 3: Mapping the Earth *(Offline)*

Review what you have learned about maps. When finished, place your completed lesson review sheet in your Science Notebook.

ASSESS

Lesson Assessment: Mapping the Earth (*Offline*)

You will complete an offline assessment covering the main objectives of this lesson. Your learning coach will score this assessment.

Name _____ Date _____

Ring of Fire

The Ring of Fire sounds much like what it describes—a region of mountain building, earthquakes, and volcanoes surrounding the Pacific Ocean. Use latitude and longitude to map the Ring of Fire by locating the volcanoes in the table below and on the next page.

Spread your wall map of the world out on the floor. Use dried beans or dried peas to plot the locations of the volcanoes on your map.

	Location	Check When Plotted
Rincon de la Vieja, Costa Rica	10° N, 85° W	
Cerro Negro, Nicaragua	12° N, 86° W	
Pacaya, Guatemala	14° N, 90° W	
Popocatepetl, Mexico	19° N, 99° W	
Mount Saint Helens, Washington	46° N, 122° W	
Amukta, Alaska	52° N, 171° W	
Kliuchevskoi, Russia	56° N, 160° E	
Ruapehu, New Zealand	39° S, 175° E	
Metis Shoal, Tonga Islands	19° S, 174° W	
Kilauea, Hawaii	19° N, 155° W	
Canlaon, Philippines	10° N, 123° E	
Papandayan, Java, Indonesia	7° S, 108° E	
Soufriere Hills, Montserrat, West Indies	16° N, 62° W	
Mayon, Philippines	13° N, 123° E	
San Cristobal, Nicaragua	12° N, 87° W	
Mount Lewotobi, Indonesia	8° S, 122° E	
Asama, Honshu, Japan	36° N, 138° E	

The Ring of Fire

	Location	Check When Plotted
Krakatau, Indonesia	6° S, 105° E	
Colima, Mexico	19° N, 103° W	
South Sister, Oregon	44° N, 121° W	
Maroa, New Zealand	38° S, 176° E	
Rotorua, New Zealand	38° S, 176° E	
Taal, Philippines	14° N, 120° E	
Shishaldin, Alaska	54° N, 163° W	
Korovin, Alaska	52° N, 174° W	
Yellowstone, Wyoming	44° N, 110° W	
Chiginagak, Alaska	57° N, 157° W	
Adatara, Honshu, Japan	37° N, 140° E	
Loihi Seamount, Hawaii	18° N, 155° W	
Long Valley Caldera, California	37° N, 118° W	
Akutan, Alaska	54° N, 166° W	
Hosho, Kyushu, Japan	33° N, 131° E	

What patterns do you see in the points that you plotted?

_____

_____

Name _____ Date _____

Mapping the Earth Lesson Review

Review what you have learned about maps. When finished, place your completed lesson review sheet in your Science Notebook.

Vocabulary Review

Use words or phrases from the Word Bank to complete each sentence.

Word Bank

closer together	prime meridian	meridians	latitude	longitude
farther apart	east	west	north	south	equator

1. Parallel lines of _____ show distances _____ and _____ of the equator.

2. The vertical lines on this map are called _____.

3. Vertical lines of _____ describe distances _____and _____of the prime meridian.

4. Lines of longitude are _____at the equator, and they are_____toward the poles.

5. Distance north and south on the globe is measured from the_____, while distance east and west on the globe is measured as distance from the _____.

Map Scale Review

Use the 'Using Map Scales' map in the Explore section of your lesson to answer the questions below.

6. How far is Martinsburg from Williamsburg? _____.

7. How far is Union from Canoe Creek State Park? _____.

Short Answer

8. A student writes the following: The place where I collected the rock sample was located at 130° E, 30° S. What is wrong with this location description?

_____

_____

_____

Name _____ Date _____

Mapping the Earth Lesson Assessment

Map Essentials

Use the map of Wallis Island below to answer the following questions. Round coordinates to the nearest whole number.

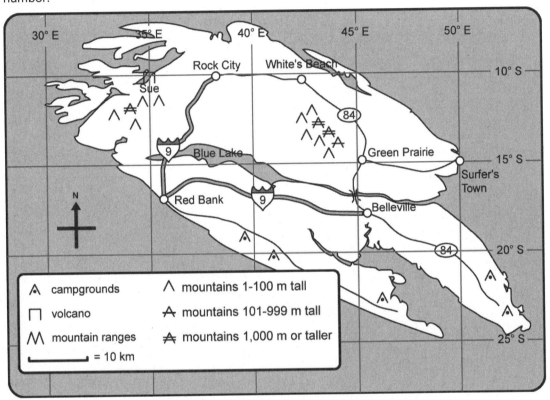

Wallis Island is located east of the prime meridian and south of the equator.

1. At what latitude and longitude would you find Sue Volcano? _____

2. At what latitude and longitude would you find Green Prairie? _____

3. At what latitude and longitude would you find Surfer's Town? _____

4. How many campgrounds are on the island? _____

5. Where is Green Prairie located in relation to White's Beach? _____

6. How many mountains are 1,000 m or taller on the island? _____

7. What is the shortest distance from Surfer's Town to Rock City? _____

8. What city on the island is farthest east? _____

Student Guide
Lesson 4: Mapping Earth's Physical Features

Who uses maps? How are they made? Geologists often use topographic maps when they're doing research. Learn about one type of map that details the rise and fall of the land.

Lesson Objectives

- Analyze topographic maps.
- Define topography as the physical features of an area of land, including mountains, valleys, plains, and bodies of water.
- Identify a topographic map as a representation of the earth's surface.

PREPARE

Approximate lesson time is 60 minutes.

Materials

For the Student

- 💻 Topo Challenge Map Key
- 💻 Lesson Review

Keywords and Pronunciation

cartographer (kahr-TAH-gruh-fuhr) : a person who makes maps

contour interval : the difference in elevation between contour lines;a contour interval of 10 meters indicates that the contour lines on the map show 10-meter differences in elevation

contour line : on a map, the line connecting points having the same elevations above sea level;contour lines that are spaced close together on a map show an area with a steep slope

elevation : distance of something above a reference point (such as sea level)

topographic (tah-puh-GRA-fihk)

topographic map (tah-puh-GRA-fihk) : a map showing elevation of land in relation to sea level; a topographic map may use contour lines to show elevation

topography (tuh-PAH-gruh-fee) : physical features of an area of land

---

LEARN
Activity 1: The Lay of the Land *(Online)*

Activity 2: Topo Challenge *(Online)*
Take the Topo Callenge!

How much practice have you had reading topographic maps? Take the Topo Challenge to find out if you are a beginner or are already an expert.

Activity 3: Mapping Earth's Physical Features *(Offline)*

Review what you have learned about topographic maps. When you're finished, place your completed lesson review sheet in your Science Notebook.

ASSESS

Lesson Assessment: Mapping Earth's Physical Features *(Online)*

You will complete an online assessment covering the main objectives of this lesson. Your assessment will be scored by the computer.

Activity 3: Mapping Earth's Physical Features

——	—500—	——	▬	••••••••
Stream	Topo Line Major	Topo Line Minor	Park Boundary	Levee
▬▬	▬▬	▭▭	——	- - - - -
Limited Access Road	Primary Road	Secondary Road	Minor Road	Trail
+++++++	✕	- - - -	⊕	95
Railroad	Airport	Channel	Bridge	Interstate
50	30	▪	▪	⚞
US Highway	State Highway	Woods	Water	Marsh
▦	▦	⬛	⚐	▪
Sand Dunes	Sand Beach	Orchard	Shipwreck	Building
⚑	✝	⌇	◎	◎
School	Church	Coral Reef	Crater	Mountain

Name _____   Date _____

Mapping Earth's Physical Features Lesson Review

Review what you have learned about topographic maps. When you're finished, place your completed lesson review sheet in your Science Notebook.

Vocabulary Review

Word Bank :

| cartographer | contour interval | contour lines | topographic map | elevation |

Use words or phrases from the word bank to complete the paragraph about topographic maps.

Topographic Maps

A _____ is designed to show the rise and fall of the landscape. _____ show how far the land rises above sea level, or its _____. The distance between two contour lines is known as the _____. A _____ carefully constructs topographic maps using information, photographs, and technology.

Map Skills

Look at the map on Screen 6 in your lesson. Then answer the questions.

1. What is the contour interval used on this map? _____

2. If the top of the map is north, which direction does the stream flow? _____

3. Which is steeper, the east slope or the west slope of the mountain? _____

4. How many buildings are shown on the map? _____

Student Guide
Lesson 5: Weathering

The earth does not look the same today as it did yesterday. Over time, many natural processes wear down the earth's landscape, causing changes. Did you know that droplets of water, chunks of ice, and gusts of wind can change the earth's landforms? Learn how they reshape the earth by breaking down rock into smaller pieces.

Lesson Objectives

- Explain that weathering produces sediments that contribute to soil formation (sand, silt, clay).
- Give examples of how climate differences influence the rate of weathering.
- Define weathering.

PREPARE

Approximate lesson time is 60 minutes.

Materials

> For the Student
>> 📖 Weathering in Action Activity Sheet
>> 📖 Weathering Lesson Review

Keywords and Pronunciation

chemical weathering : the breaking up of rocks by chemical reactions; natural acids dissolved in rainwater are important agents of chemical weathering of rocks

ice wedging : a type of mechanical weathering in which water seeps into the cracks in a rock, freezes and expands, and splits the rock apart

lichen (LIY-kuhn) : a life form which grows as crusty patches on soil, rocks, and trees; lichen forms when an alga and a fungus grow together

mechanical weathering : the breaking up of rocks by physical forces; mechanical weathering occurs when water expands as it freezes in the crack of a rock, expanding the crack and breaking the rock apart

weathering : the breakdown of rocks by physical or chemical processes; weathering causes the rocks on a cliff to wear away

LEARN
Activity 1: Earth Wears Down *(Online)*

Activity 2: Weathering in Action *(Offline)*

In this activity, you will find examples of weathering in your community. Print the worksheet and explore your world! If you're unable to work outside, use the websites below to examine weathering photos.

Weathering - Part 1

Weathering - Part 2

Activity 3: Weathering *(Offline)*

Review what you have learned about weathering. When finished, place your completed lesson review sheet in your Science Notebook.

ASSESS

Lesson Assessment: Weathering, Part 1 *(Online)*

You will complete an online assessment covering the main objectives of this lesson. Your assessment will be scored by the computer.

Lesson Assessment: Weathering, Part 2 *(Offline)*

You will complete an offline assessment covering the main objectives of this lesson. Your learning coach will score this assessment.

Name _____   Date _____

Weathering in Action Activity Sheet

You can see science in action all around you. In this activity, you will observe weathering.

Procedure

Go outside and look at different rocks and building materials. Examine each for evidence of weathering and use the data table to record what you see.

Materials (optional)

• camera

Data Collection

In the table below, make a check mark for each example of weathering. Use the blank rows to add other examples of weathering.

Signs of Weathering	Observed	
	Yes	No
Flakes of brick		
Cracks in rocks		
Lichen growing on rocks		
Roots or plant growth making cracks in concrete		
Worn away statues		
Exposed rocks		
Rust on rocks		

Analysis

Record your observations and answers to the following questions and place your work in your Science Notebook.

1. Choose three examples of weathering to sketch below. Classify each example as mechanical weathering, chemical weathering, or both. Check the Explore section of your lesson to review the different types of weathering.

Example 1	Example 2	Example 3
Types of weathering:	Types of weathering:	Types of weathering:

Weathering in Action Activity Sheet

Science Club Idea:

Plan a trip to observe examples of weathering in your area. Work in small groups and see which team can identify the most examples. Remember that weathering can be found everywhere, from creeks and forests to cities and towns. Sand, soil, and pieces of rock are results of weathering.

Name _____ Date _____

Weathering Lesson Review

Review what you have learned about weathering. When finished, place your completed lesson review sheet in your Science Notebook.

Making a Venn Diagram

A Venn diagram is a special tool to help you compare different ideas that have some things in common. Use the words or phrases from the Word Bank to fill in the Venn diagram below. Put words or phrases relating to chemical weathering in the right circle and words or phrases having to do with mechanical weathering in the left circle. Words or phrases relating to both mechanical and chemical weathering should be placed in the area marked "Both."

Word Bank

breaks down rocks into small pieces	can be caused by acids in rain water	plant roots
causes physical changes	changes the earth's landscape	ice wedging
causes chemical changes in rocks	can cause rust on some rocks	
small pieces of sand, silt, and clay become soil		

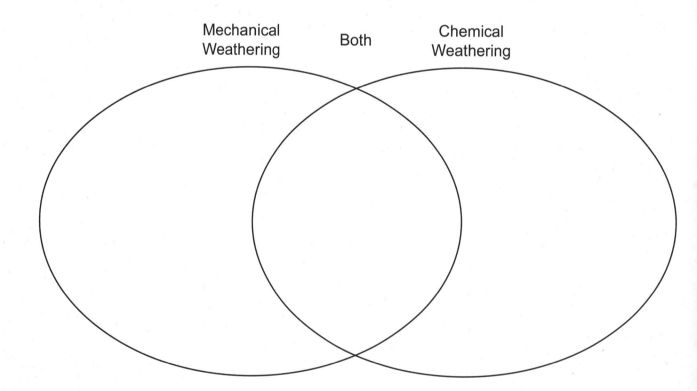

Mechanical Weathering   Both   Chemical Weathering

Name _____   Date _____

Weathering, Part 2 Lesson Assessment

Answer the questions below. Ask an adult to use the answer key to score the assessment. Then enter the results online.

10 pts. **1.** Describe the process of soil formation. _____

_____

_____

_____

_____

_____

_____

_____

_____

_____

10 pts. **2.** Explain why weathering occurs more quickly in tropical rain forests. _____

_____

_____

_____

_____

_____

_____

_____

_____

_____

Student Guide
Lesson 6: Erosion

We often think of the earth's surface as unchanging. Hills and valleys look much the same every day. Actually, though, the earth's surface is always changing. Some changes happen quickly. For example, during landslides, hundreds of tons of rock and soil may slide down a hill in only a few minutes. By contrast, a river may wear away solid rock slowly, over millions of years. Although these events may seem very different, they are both examples of the same process: erosion.

Lesson Objectives

- Describe major causes, processes, and consequences of erosion.
- Define erosion.
- Identify surface structures that show the effects of erosion.

PREPARE

Approximate lesson time is 60 minutes.

Advance Preparation

- You will need to go outside to complete this activity. If you are not able to go outside, complete the activity inside using a large plastic tub.
- You will need to save some sand for the Lab:Desertification lesson.

Materials

For the Student

books
household item
sand
baking dish
measuring cup
water

💻 Erosion Lesson Review

Keywords and Pronunciation

agent : a force or material that causes a change

deposition : the process in which rock and soil particles move from water, wind, or ice onto the land

erosion : the gradual removal of the surface of the land by water, wind, or glaciers

glacier (GLAY-shur) : large moving masses of ice and snow on land

mass wasting : the downhill movement of rock and soil; also known as mass movement

meander (mee-AN-duhr) : a turn or winding of a stream or river; as a river ages, reaching a flat area, it tends to form meanders as it flows back and forth across the landscape

rivulet (RIH-vyuh-luht) : a small stream; a rivulet often flows into a larger stream

---

LEARN
Activity 1: Erosion *(Online)*

Activity 2: Fast-Forward Erosion *(Offline)*

Erosion is normally a very slow process. Try to speed the process up by making it happen in your kitchen sink.

Materials

large, glass baking dish

sand

measuring cup

books

water

Procedure

1. Fill a large, glass baking dish half full of sand.

2. Slowly pour water over the sand until the sand is saturated. Be careful not to add too much. Pools of water should not form. Smooth the sand out to form a smooth, flat surface.

3. Take the baking dish outside. Create a slope by propping it up with a few books underneath one side.

4. Position the measuring cup over the higher side of the sand.

5. Very slowly turn the measuring cup so that only a small, steady stream of water trickles onto the wet sand.

6. Answer the following questions while you make observations.

7. Try repeating the activity, except use the kitchen faucet instead of a measuring cup.

Questions

1. Where is the sand eroded? How quickly is the water flowing there?

_____

_____

_____

_____

2. Where is the sand transported? Where is it deposited?

_____

_____

_____

_____

3. What shape are the channels made by the flowing water?

_____

_____

_____

_____

4. A river delta is a deposit of sand and soil at the mouth of a river. What shape is the delta at the end of the "rivers"?

_____

_____

_____

Science Club Idea

Try looking for examples of erosion in your area. Examples can be seen in parks or wooded areas, along streams and creeks, and among sand dunes.

Activity 3: Erosion (Offline)

Review what you have learned about erosion. When finished, place your completed lesson review sheet in your Science Notebook.

ASSESS

Lesson Assessment: Erosion, Part 1 (Online)

You will complete an online assessment covering the main objectives of this lesson. Your assessment will be scored by the computer.

Lesson Assessment: Erosion, Part 2 (Offline)

You will complete an offline assessment covering the main objectives of this lesson. Your learning coach will score this assessment.

Name _____ Date _____

Erosion Lesson Review

Review what you have learned about erosion. When finished, place your completed lesson review sheet in your Science Notebook.

Erosion Notes

Using tables to take notes can help organize details of new information. Find the information from the lesson to fill in the table below.

Cause of erosion	Example(s) of where it occurs	Example(s) of feature(s) it forms
		meanders, cliffs, valleys, canyons
wind		
	areas near the poles or mountaintops	U-shaped valleys

1. Erosion and weathering are often confused. How is erosion different from weathering? _____

_____

_____

_____

_____

⚙ Assessment

Name _____   Date _____

Erosion, Part 2 Lesson Assessment

Read each question carefully, and then write your answer in the space below each one.

10 pts. **1.** Explain why glaciers are called nature's bulldozers. In your answer, give examples of
how land is reshaped by glaciers _____

_____

_____

_____

_____

_____

_____

_____

_____

_____

_____

_____

_____

_____

_____

_____

10 pts. **2.** Liquid water is the most common agent of erosion. Make a labeled drawing below to
show how rivers and streams play a part in erosion as water moves through them.

Student Guide
Lesson 7: Soils of the Earth

All soil has its beginnings in rocks. Over time, large rocks are weathered by precipitation and other physical processes. The rocks are also broken down by chemical processes. These various processes break the rocks into smaller and smaller pieces, ultimately to form the beginnings of soil. Depending on the climate and the original type of rock, different types of soils can form.

Lesson Objectives

- Explain how soil is formed.
- Describe the three major soil types: sand, silt, and clay.
- Relate soil types to climate.

PREPARE

Approximate lesson time is 60 minutes.

Materials

For the Student

- Graph Paper
- Working with Scientific Data
- pencils, colored 12
- Soils of the Earth Lesson Review

Keywords and Pronunciation

biome (BIY-ohm) : a large area dominated by characteristic plants and animals, such as a rain forest, desert, or tundra

chemical weathering : the breaking up of rocks by chemical reactions; natural acids dissolved in rainwater are important agents of chemical weathering of rocks

lichen (LIY-kuhn) : a life form which grows as crusty patches on soil, rocks, and trees; lichen forms when an alga and a fungus grow together

loam : a type of soil that has equal parts of sand, silt, and clay; many plants grow well in loam

permeability (puhr-mee-uh-BIH-luh-tee) : the rate at which water passes through a material

porosity (puh-RAH-suh-tee) : the measure of the space between particles in rock or soil; the porosity of soil allows it to soak up rainwater

---

LEARN
Activity 1: Soils of the Earth *(Online)*

Activity 2: Working with Scientific Data *(Online)*

Studying scientific measurements can help you understand relationships in science. Work with temperature data to investigate how air temperature relates to soil temperature.

Activity 3: Soils of the Earth *(Online)*

Review what you have learned about soils of the earth. When finished, place your completed lesson review sheet in your Science Notebook.

ASSESS

Lesson Assessment: Soils of the Earth, Part 1 *(Online)*

You will complete an online assessment covering the main objectives of this lesson. Your assessment will be scored by the computer.

Lesson Assessment: Soils of the Earth, Part 2 *(Offline)*

You will complete an offline assessment covering the main objectives of this lesson. Your learning coach will score this assessment.

Name _____   Date _____

Graph Paper

Key

air temperature =

soil temperature =

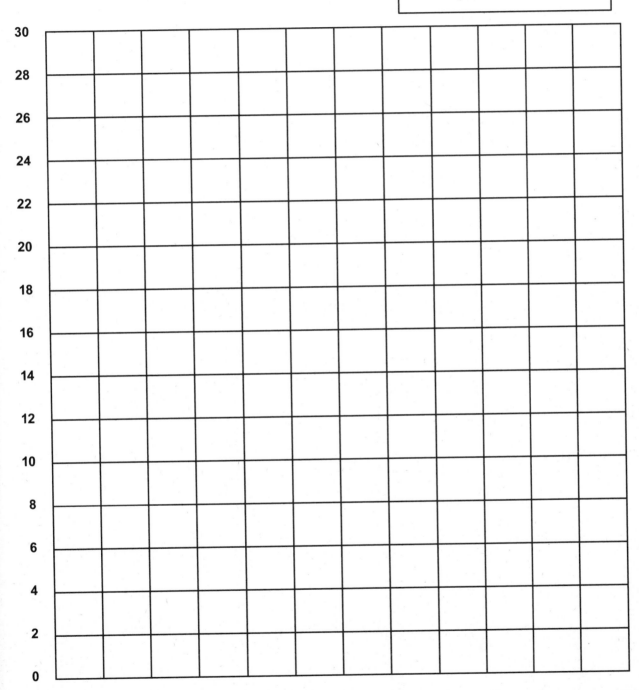

Name _____   Date _____

Working with Scientific Data Air and Soil Temperature

Working with Scientific Data

Soil temperature is of interest to scientists in the field of agriculture. Plants grow best in soil within a certain range of temperatures and most will stop growing at soil temperatures under 10 degrees Celsius (50 degrees Fahrenheit). Temperature affects how fast plants and other organisms grow and how fast dead organisms decay, which contributes to soil quality. The helpful effects of soil organisms only occur in warm soil.

Growing plants and crops must be protected from major changes in soil temperature. Using shade or surface cover can keep soil cool. Water allows heat to flow more easily in and throughout soil. Mulch acts like insulation for soil. It keeps soil cool in the summer and warm in the winter. Even the direction the soil faces influences soil temperature. The coolest slopes face north, followed by east, west, and south-facing soil.

How does air temperature affect soil temperature? Work with scientific data to examine how they are related.

Materials

- Air and Soil Temperature Data
- graph paper
- pencil
- colored Pencils

Procedure

Study the Air and Soil Temperature Data. The data set was taken over a period of 24 hours by a network of environmental monitoring stations designed by scientists at the University of Oklahoma. Follow the steps below to create a line graph of the data.

1. On your graph paper, label the bottom axis "Time of Observation.".
2. Label the side axis "Temperature in Degrees Celsius"
3. Using a different color for air and soil, create a line graph showing the change in their temperatures over time.
4. In the key, show which color you used for air and for temperature.
5. Answer the questions in the Data Analysis section. Use the tips below if you need to.

Air and Soil Temperature Data

Station	Date	Time	Temperature, Air at 1.5 m	Temperature, Soil at 10 cm
			degrees Celsius	degrees Celsius
Burneyville, OK	11/16/99	12:00 am	10.1	17.0
Burneyville, OK	11/16/99	2:00 am	8.3	15.9
Burneyville, OK	11/16/99	4:00 am	6.8	14.9
Burneyville, OK	11/16/99	6:00 am	5.6	14
Burneyville, OK	11/16/99	8:00 am	5.3	13.2
Burneyville, OK	11/16/99	10:00 am	12.3	13.0
Burneyville, OK	11/16/99	12:00 pm	21.2	15.6
Burneyville, OK	11/16/99	2:00 pm	25.5	19.5
Burneyville, OK	11/16/99	4:00 pm	26.5	22.3
Burneyville, OK	11/16/99	6:00 pm	24.3	21.9
Burneyville, OK	11/16/99	8:00 pm	19.9	19.8
Burneyville, OK	11/16/99	10:00 pm	13.1	18.4
Burneyville, OK	11/17/99	12:00 am	10.8	17.1

Tips

Converting Temperature:

Here's how to convert Celsius to Fahrenheit:
1. Begin by multiplying the Celsius temperature by 9.
2. Divide the answer by 5.
3. Now add 32.

You can also use an online converter at www.sciencemadesimple.com.

Finding range:

Determine the highest and lowest temperatures and subtract the second number from the first.

Data Analysis

1. When air temperature increased, what happened to soil temperature? When air temperature decreased, what happened to soil temperature?

   _____

   _____

   _____

2. Describe what would happen to both air temperature and soil temperature if cold weather were to pass through the area.

   _____

   _____

   _____

3. What can you learn about soil and air from looking at your graphs and your answers above?

   _____

   _____

   _____

   _____

Conclusion

What does the data mean for people involved in farming and agriculture?

_____

_____

_____

_____

Science Club Idea

Plant a community garden and test different methods of controlling soil temperature. Try mulch and a surface cover and compare it to an uncovered patch of soil. Take measurements of the soil temperature at a set time in the morning and evening for 10 days, then compare your measurements.

Name _____   Date _____

Soils of the Earth Lesson Review

Review what you have learned about soils of the earth. When finished, place your completed lesson review sheet in your Science Notebook.

Field Notes

Below are some notes taken during observations of soil samples of silt, sand, and clay. Refer back to the lesson to answer the questions below, based on the notes.

Sample 1

Very little water passed through the sample during the observation.

The sample felt sticky. The grains were small.

Sample 2

Felt gritty. Grains were larger than in Sample 1.

Most water was absorbed but most of it passed through this soil very quickly.

Sample 3

Felt soft and floury. Grains were smaller than in Sample 2 but larger than in Sample 1. Appeared nutrient-rich.

Water was absorbed. Some passed through during the observation.

Which Sample:

1. Has high porosity and low permeability? _____

2. Has low porosity and high permeability? _____

3. Seems best suited for growing plants? _____

4. Is likely clay soil? _____

5. Is likely sandy soil? _____

6. Is likely silt? _____

Name _____   Date _____

Soils of the Earth, Part 2 Lesson Assessment

Read the questions, then answer them in the space provided.

(10 pts.)

1. Describe some actions that may play a role in the process of soil formation.

_____

_____

_____

_____

_____

_____

(10 pts.)

2. Name a biome that is likely to have fertile soil and explain why.

_____

_____

_____

_____

_____

_____

Student Guide
Lesson 8: Soil Profiles

Soil is spread in a very thin layer over the surface of the earth, and scientists have identified thousands of different soils.

Soil is important for many reasons. It is a habitat for a variety of organisms and the support system for plants. In this lesson you will learn more about soil's distinct layers and characteristics.

Lesson Objectives

- Investigate and identify the composition of different soils.
- Describe a soil profile, including soil horizons.
- Explain how plants use various components of soils (organic and inorganic).

PREPARE

Approximate lesson time is 60 minutes.

Materials

For the Student

📇 Soil Profiles Lesson Review

Keywords and Pronunciation

horizon : a soil layer

humus (HYOO-muhs) : the dark portion of soil created by the decay of plant and animal matter

inorganic : non-living

leaching : the process in which water carries nutrients from one layer of soil to a lower layer of soil

nitrogen : a nutrient critical for plant growth

organic : living or once living

soil profile : cross-section of the soil layers above the bedrock

LEARN
Activity 1: Sink Down in the Soil *(Online)*

Activity 2: Soil Profiles *(Online)*

Review what you have learned about soil profiles. When finished, place your completed lesson review sheet in your Science Notebook.

ASSESS

Lesson Assessment: Soil Profiles (*Online*)

You will complete an offline assessment covering the main objectives of this lesson. Your learning coach will score this assessment.

Name _____   Date _____

Soil Profiles Lesson Review

Review what you have learned about soil profiles. When finished, place your completed lesson review sheet in your Science Notebook.

Use the illustration of soil profiles in the Explore section to match the soil profile with the characteristic. Write "A" for Horizon A, "B" for Horizon B, "C" for Horizon C, and "Bedrock" for bedrock

_____ 1. High in nutrients and light in color.

_____ 2. Mostly weathered rock.

_____ 3. Crumbly and dark

_____ 4. Little organic matter, because of leaching.

_____ 5. Below the C horizon.

_____ 6. Contains humus

_____ 7. Where plant roots grow

_____ 8. Lies between soil above and rock below

_____ 9. Layer on which all soil sits

Lesson Assessment

Draw a diagram *(20 pts.)*

1. Draw a soil profile showing A, B, and C horizons. Label each horizon and the bedrock. Write a description of each horizon next to the label.

Short Answer (6 pts.)

2. Name some examples of organic and inorganic matter in soils that plants need to grow.

_____

_____

_____

_____

_____

_____

_____

Student Guide
Lesson 9: Lab: Desertification

In parts of the world where water is scarce and vegetation is thin, wind is a powerful force that alters the landscape. Blowing on the desert sand, wind can shape large hills, known as sand dunes, which sometimes cover fertile fields and even houses. Find out about how sand dunes can affect people in cities and towns, and then investigate methods of protection against advancing sand dunes.

Lesson Objectives

- Record scientific data using charts, graphs, and/or written descriptions.
- Explain how sand dunes are formed and recognize that they have two sides: leeward and windward.
- Conduct an experiment to determine the most effective method for reducing the advancement of sand dunes and deposition of sand in populated areas.
- Record scientific data using charts, graphs, and/or written descriptions.

PREPARE

Approximate lesson time is 60 minutes.

Advance Preparation

- If your sand is moist, open 2 days ahead of time. Put in a shallow pan in a warm place to make sure it's dry. Stir it a couple times a day.

Materials

For the Student

- 🖳 Graph Paper
- 🖳 Slowing Down Desertification
- aluminum baking dish - 9 x 13
- modeling clay
- ruler (metric & customary)
- sand, fine
- tub, plastic
- aluminum foil
- coins
- craft sticks
- graduated cylinder
- hair dryer
- oil, cooking
- pipe cleaners
- safety goggles
- scissors
- tape - masking
- toothpicks

Keywords and Pronunciation

desertification (dih-ZUHR-tuh-fuh-KAY-shuhn) : loss of productivity of land in relatively dry areas, usually due to human activities that cause damage to the vegetation, but sometimes due to climatic change

drought (drowt) : period of particularly dry weather, bad enough to affect people's lives or the environment

dune : a hill or ridge of wind-blown sand

leeward : on or toward the side to which the wind is blowing

windward : of or on the side exposed to the wind or to prevailing winds

---

LEARN

Activity 1: Pre-Lab: Erosion and Sand Dunes (Online)

Activity 2: Can We Slow the Dunes? (Offline)

As you have learned, advancing sand dunes and blowing sand can be a huge problem. Conduct this experiment to determine what protection method will be most effective at slowing the deposition of sand into a miniature town.

Science Club Idea

This is a great activity to do with a partner or in a small group. Plan a science afternoon and get together with other students to complete the lab. Or, suggest to your teacher an online get-together with other students in your school to discuss the different outcomes.

Safety

Electrical appliances must be in good condition. Never allow an electrical appliance to contact water. If one falls into water, do not reach in for it. Turn off power at the panel board or fuse box. Unplug the appliance from the wall by grasping the plug, not the cord. Contact an adult immediately.

When using scissors, knives, or any sharp instrument, always carry them with tips and points facing down and away from you. Cut away from yourself. Never try to catch falling sharp objects. Hold sharp instruments only by the handles. If you cut yourself, notify an adult immediately.

ASSESS

Lesson Assessment: Lab: Desertification (*Offline*)

Have an adult review your answers to the Slowing Down Desertification lab, and input the results online.

Name

Date

Graph Paper

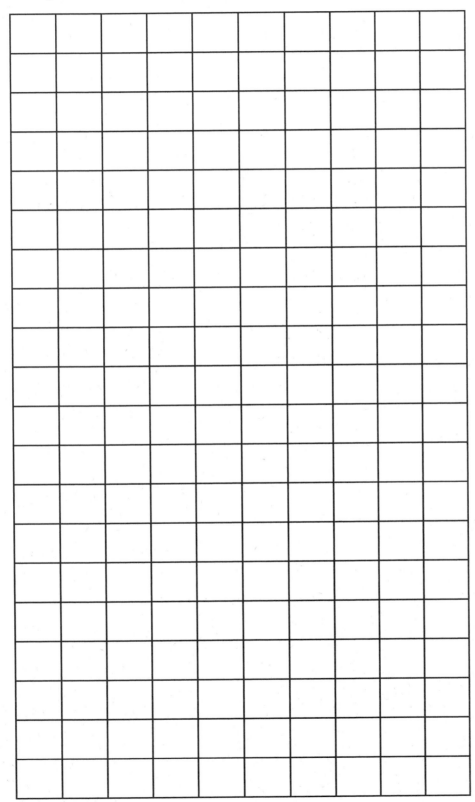

Name

Date

Slowing Down Desertification

Purpose:

During this lab activity, you will determine how to solve a problem by comparing methods of slowing down effects of desertification. These methods are the use of short vegetation and tall vegetation, straw grids, and fences. You will want to do this activity on a non-carpeted floor because it involves blowing sand.

State the Problem: In your own words, state the problem you are trying to solve.

_____

_____

_____

_____

Materials

- disposable aluminum pan, 9" x 13"
- aluminum foil
- sand
- modeling clay
- hair dryer with cool setting
- cooking spray (oil)
- pipe cleaners
- ruler
- scissors
- toothpicks
- craft sticks
- tape
- coins
- graduated cylinder
- plastic tub
- Science Notebook
- SAFETY GOGGLES

Safety Stop

Have you read the safety information for this lab activity? If not, return to the lesson and do so now.

Procedure

Part A: Constructing the Town and Dune

1. Using scissors, cut out one of the ends of the aluminum baking dish. This is the front of the pan.

2. Measure a distance of 16 cm from the back of the pan. Line the back portion of the dish with aluminum foil. Let the foil extend about 10 cm above the height of the pan to catch any flying sand.

3. Tape a few coins under the front edge of the foil to keep the foil weighted down.

4. Using modeling clay, create a few small blocks, approximately 3 cm high, to represent buildings in the affected community.

5. Place the clay buildings on the aluminum foil, approximately 10 cm from the uncut end of the dish.

6. Add a few cups full of sand to the open side of the baking dish. The sand should not be on the aluminum foil.

7. Mold a small dune with this sand about 14 cm away from the buildings. The top of the dune should span the entire width of the pan and should be as high as the buildings. \

8. Set up a plastic tub behind the foil to catch the sand (if needed).

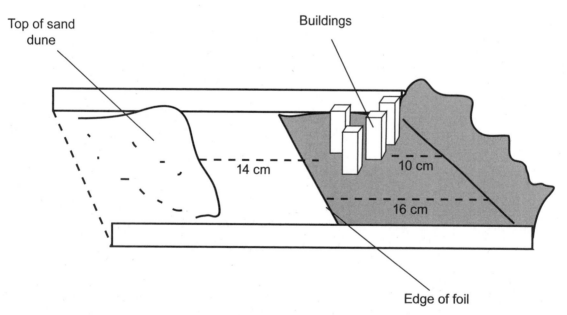

The town and the dune

Part B: Protection Methods

In this section, you will test six protection methods separately. Follow the steps to prepare them.

1. No protection; no preparation.

2. Short vegetation: Make short vegetation by cutting 10 pipe cleaners to a height of 3 cm.

3. Tall vegetation: Make tall vegetation by cutting 10 pipe cleaners to a height of 8 cm.

4. Straw grids—Place toothpicks in the sand so there is approximately 1 cm of space between them.

5. Sand fences: Make sand fences by breaking 10 craft sticks in half. When you test this method, put the broken ends in the sand.

6. Oil: Find a can of spray-type cooking oil. When testing this method, spray a light coat on the sand.

7. Move the pipe cleaners, craft sticks, toothpicks, and spray oil to the side.

Part C: Testing

You will need to follow these steps for each of the protection methods:

8. Position the hair dryer at the open end of the dish, aimed at the clay buildings.

9. Put on your safety goggles to protect your eyes from flying sand.

10. Turn on the hair dryer at a cool low setting for 25 seconds. Move the hair dryer (wind source) closer if needed. (Note: it is possible that taller plant protection could be "knocked over" by the wind. It is fine if this happens.)

11. After 25 seconds, turn off the hair dryer and remove the buildings.

12. Very carefully, lift up the aluminum foil carrying the sand that blew from the dune into the town.

13. Slowly pour the sand from the aluminum foil into a dry graduated cylinder.

14. Record the volume of sand in the Data Table.

15. Carefully pour all the sand from the graduated cylinder back onto the dune in the pan.

16. Replace the foil and place the buildings in their original position.

17. Make sure the dune is still as tall as the buildings.

18. Repeat this process with each protection method, placing each protection device on the leeward side of the dune, about 8 cm in front of the town and evenly spaced. You may use extra clay to anchor the pipe cleaners and sticks.

19. Remember to keep these three things the same for each try:

- the height of the dune (about 3 cm)

- the distance of the dune from the town (14 cm)

- the distance of the protection from the town (8 cm)

20. After completing the Data Table, move on to the Analysis and Questions sections.

Data Table – Observations

Record your measurements of sand in the table below.

Method	Distance from town (cm)	Length of wind (sec)	Volume of sand blown into town (ml)
No protection			
Short vegetation			
Tall vegetation			
Straw grids			
Sand fence			
Oil			

Analysis

Analyze your data by creating a bar graph.

1. Print the Graph Paper if you have not already done so.

2. Label the horizontal axis "Protection Method."

3. Label the vertical axis "Volume of Sand (in ml)" and number it from 1–25.

4. Create a bar showing the amount of sand collected for each method.

Conclusion

Answer the questions based on your data. When you're finished, store the lab in your Science Notebook.

1. Which method was most effective at leaving the town protected and unaffected by the sand? Explain using your data and the bar graph that you constructed.

_____

_____

_____

_____

2. Is this method something real towns should use? Why or why not?

_____

_____

_____

_____

3. Besides the no protection method, which method was least effective? Again, use your data and bar graph to support your answer.

_____

_____

_____

_____

4. During this experiment, you only conducted one trial. Scientists usually repeat their trials. Why do you think they do that?

_____

_____

_____

_____

5. Why did you test a "no protection" method?

_____

_____

_____

_____

6. Why was it important to keep the height of the dune, the distance of the dune from the town, and the distance of the protection from the town the same for each test?

_____

_____

_____

_____

Name _____   Date _____

Lab: Desertification Lesson Assessment

For the questions below, review your student's responses on the Slowing Down Desertification Lab and input the results online.

1. Follow the procedures in the attached Slowing Down Desertification Lab to determine what protection method will be most effective at slowing the deposition of sand into a miniature town.

2. Based on the data you gathered during the experiment, complete the Analysis section of the attached Slowing Down Desertification Lab.

3. Based on the data you gathered during the experiment, answer the questions in the Conclusion section of the attached Slowing Down Desertification Lab.

Name _____ Date _____

Slowing Down Desertification

Purpose:

During this lab activity, you will determine how to solve a problem by comparing methods of slowing down effects of desertification. These methods are the use of short vegetation and tall vegetation, straw grids, and fences. You will want to do this activity on a non-carpeted floor because it involves blowing sand.

State the Problem: In your own words, state the problem you are trying to solve.

_____

_____

_____

_____

Materials

- disposable aluminum pan, 9" x 13"
- aluminum foil
- sand
- modeling clay
- hair dryer with cool setting
- cooking spray (oil)
- pipe cleaners
- ruler
- scissors
- toothpicks
- craft sticks
- tape
- coins
- graduated cylinder
- plastic tub
- Science Notebook
- SAFETY GOGGLES

Safety Stop

Have you read the safety information for this lab activity? If not, return to the lesson and do so now.

Procedure

Part A: Constructing the Town and Dune

1. Using scissors, cut out one of the ends of the aluminum baking dish. This is the front of the pan.

2. Measure a distance of 16 cm from the back of the pan. Line the back portion of the dish with aluminum foil. Let the foil extend about 10 cm above the height of the pan to catch any flying sand.

3. Tape a few coins under the front edge of the foil to keep the foil weighted down.

4. Using modeling clay, create a few small blocks, approximately 3 cm high, to represent buildings in the affected community.

5. Place the clay buildings on the aluminum foil, approximately 10 cm from the uncut end of the dish.

6. Add a few cups full of sand to the open side of the baking dish. The sand should not be on the aluminum foil.

7. Mold a small dune with this sand about 14 cm away from the buildings. The top of the dune should span the entire width of the pan and should be as high as the buildings. \

8. Set up a plastic tub behind the foil to catch the sand (if needed).

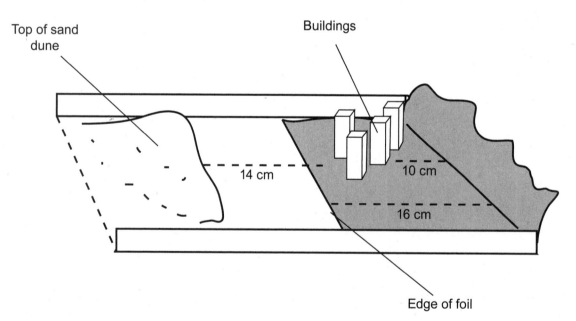

The town and the dune

Part B: Protection Methods

In this section, you will test six protection methods separately. Follow the steps to prepare them.

1. No protection; no preparation.

2. Short vegetation: Make short vegetation by cutting 10 pipe cleaners to a height of 3 cm.

3. Tall vegetation: Make tall vegetation by cutting 10 pipe cleaners to a height of 8 cm.

4. Straw grids—Place toothpicks in the sand so there is approximately 1 cm of space between them.

5. Sand fences: Make sand fences by breaking 10 craft sticks in half. When you test this method, put the broken ends in the sand.

6. Oil: Find a can of spray-type cooking oil. When testing this method, spray a light coat on the sand.

7. Move the pipe cleaners, craft sticks, toothpicks, and spray oil to the side.

Part C: Testing

You will need to follow these steps for each of the protection methods:

8. Position the hair dryer at the open end of the dish, aimed at the clay buildings.

9. Put on your safety goggles to protect your eyes from flying sand.

10. Turn on the hair dryer at a cool low setting for 25 seconds. Move the hair dryer (wind source) closer if needed. (Note: it is possible that taller plant protection could be "knocked over" by the wind. It is fine if this happens.)

11. After 25 seconds, turn off the hair dryer and remove the buildings.

12. Very carefully, lift up the aluminum foil carrying the sand that blew from the dune into the town.

13. Slowly pour the sand from the aluminum foil into a dry graduated cylinder.

14. Record the volume of sand in the Data Table.

15. Carefully pour all the sand from the graduated cylinder back onto the dune in the pan.

16. Replace the foil and place the buildings in their original position.

17. Make sure the dune is still as tall as the buildings.

18. Repeat this process with each protection method, placing each protection device on the leeward side of the dune, about 8 cm in front of the town and evenly spaced. You may use extra clay to anchor the pipe cleaners and sticks.

19. Remember to keep these three things the same for each try:

- the height of the dune (about 3 cm)

- the distance of the dune from the town (14 cm)

- the distance of the protection from the town (8 cm)

20. After completing the Data Table, move on to the Analysis and Questions sections.

Data Table – Observations

Record your measurements of sand in the table below.

Method	Distance from town (cm)	Length of wind (sec)	Volume of sand blown into town (ml)
No protection			
Short vegetation			
Tall vegetation			
Straw grids			
Sand fence			
Oil			

Analysis

Analyze your data by creating a bar graph.

1. Print the Graph Paper if you have not already done so.

2. Label the horizontal axis "Protection Method."

3. Label the vertical axis "Volume of Sand (in ml)" and number it from 1–25.

4. Create a bar showing the amount of sand collected for each method.

Conclusion

Answer the questions based on your data. When you're finished, store the lab in your Science Notebook.

1. Which method was most effective at leaving the town protected and unaffected by the sand? Explain using your data and the bar graph that you constructed.

_____

_____

_____

_____

2. Is this method something real towns should use? Why or why not?

_____

_____

_____

_____

3. Besides the no protection method, which method was least effective? Again, use your data and bar graph to support your answer.

_____

_____

_____

_____

4. During this experiment, you only conducted one trial. Scientists usually repeat their trials. Why do you think they do that?

_____

_____

_____

_____

5. Why did you test a "no protection" method?

_____

_____

_____

_____

6. Why was it important to keep the height of the dune, the distance of the dune from the town, and the distance of the protection from the town the same for each test?

_____

_____

_____

_____

Student Guide
Lesson 10. Optional: Your Choice

Lesson Objectives

- Practice skills and reinforce concepts taught in this course.

PREPARE

Approximate lesson time is 60 minutes.

Student Guide
Lesson 11: Unit Review

Prepare for the unit assessment by reviewing your knowledge of the earth's physical systems, mapping techniques, weathering, and soil on an exploration of an unfamiliar land. Then experience what a cartographer does as you use data to map an unmapped island.

Lesson Objectives

- Describe the basic components of the Earth's physical systems: the atmosphere, biosphere, lithosphere, hydrosphere, and magnetosphere.
- Explain latitude and longitude and recognize them as providing a primary coordinate system for reference to places on the earth.
- Describe features on maps such as coordinate systems, scales, directional indicators, keys, symbols, and contour lines.
- Describe specific uses of topographic maps.
- Describe the major processes that break apart and move material around on the earth's surface to form soil from rock and organic material and to change the shape of the surface.
- Describe major agents of mechanical weathering and of chemical weathering, how the agents cause each kind of weathering, and how mechanical weathering and chemical weathering interact to enhance each other's effects.
- Describe major types of soil in terms of porosity, permeability, and climates in which they are found.

PREPARE

Approximate lesson time is 60 minutes.

Materials

For the Student

- ▣ Earth's Surface Unit Review
- ▣ Mapping Mystery Island
- ▣ Mystery Island

LEARN
Activity 1: Where in the World? *(Online)*

Print the Earth's Surface Unit Review sheet. Read the lesson carefully, answering the questions based on what you read and have learned in the Earth's Surface unit.

Activity 2: Mapping an Island *(Online)*

Even in the twenty-first century, some areas remain unexplored. Imagine you are part of a team that has just landed on an unmapped island. What might be on this island, and how could you capture that information on a map? What advice would you give to others who will visit the island?

Name _____   Date _____

Mystery Island

Name of Map: _____

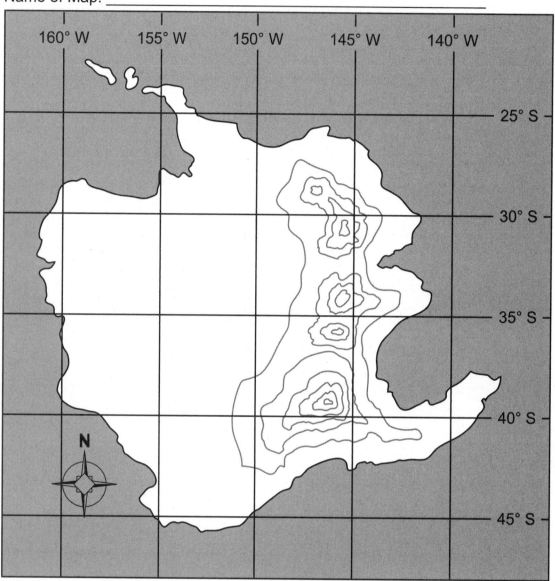

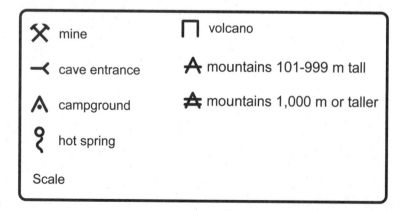

✗ mine		∏ volcano
⊰ cave entrance		A mountains 101-999 m tall
A campground		A mountains 1,000 m or taller
⚇ hot spring		

Scale

Name _____   Date _____

Mapping Mystery Island

Welcome to Mystery Island (a newly discovered, not-yet-named island). As one of the few visitors to this mystery land, it is your job to create a map of the place. Since you are a new cartographer, there are a few things you should know:

- Cartographers work closely with many people: surveyors, geologists, and other professionals who are involved in conservation, planning, and development.

- To produce maps, information is needed from many sources such as aerial photographs, field records, historical manuscripts, as well as reports and already existing maps.

- Cartographers can produce many types of maps, including road maps, tourist maps, and topographic maps.

- Cartographers are skilled at drawing, mathematics, understanding spaces, and working with details.

Procedure

Your job is to provide a map of the island that can be used by tourists. Use the clues and data below to produce an accurate map.

1. Aerial photographs show mountains along the east coast of the island at its highest point. The mountains range from 101 m to 2,000 m tall. Draw these mountains on the map and name them however you would like.

2. A geologist has provided information that a volcano in the mountains is extinct. This may be a great place for sightseeing. Place a volcano in the mountains. Name the volcano.

3. A river runs from the mountains at 147° W longitude, 28° S latitude and empties into a lake at 153° W longitude, 36° S latitude. The river then flows out to sea. Add the river and lake to the map and name them.

4. Field surveys show that a few flat areas along the west coast would be good for campgrounds. Draw them on the map.

5. 5° of longitude or latitude equals about 563 km. Use this information and a ruler to create a scale to use with this map. Draw and label your scale next to the word *Scale* in the legend.

6. Select a name for this island based on its features.

Name _____   Date _____

Earth's Surface Unit Review

In this unit, you have learned several things about the earth's surface. As you read about Antarctica, answer the questions below to review what you have learned. You may have to think hard to answer some of them, but you should be able to answer all of them. Refer to the lesson number next to each question if you need more help or you need to review a concept.

1. How would temperature changes in the atmosphere, enough to melt Antarctic ice, affect the hydrosphere, lithosphere, and biosphere? (Lesson 2)

    _____

    _____

2. Cold-weather tourists may view a spectacular display of lights. What are these lights called? Which of the earth's spheres is responsible for producing them? (Lesson 2)

    _____

    _____

3. View the topographic map of Antarctica on screen 8. Click the '+' signs to find the locations below. Use latitude and longitude to tell the location of the following sites to the nearest 5 degrees.(Lesson 3)

    a.   Amery Ice Shelf _____

    b.   Esperanza Station _____

    c.   Weddell Sea _____

4. View the topographic map of Antarctica on screen 8. What is the best use of this type of map? (Lesson 4)

    _____

    _____

5. Using contour lines, describe the rise and fall of the land in Antarctica. (Lesson 4)

    _____

    _____

6. Which type of weathering is more likely to occur in Antarctica: ice wedging or root pry? Explain. (Lesson 5)

    _____

    _____

7. Chemical weathering occurs faster in warm, tropical climates, although it happens in cold climates as well. Describe some conditions in Antarctica that could lead to chemical weathering. (Lesson 5)

_____

8. How might chemical weathering make it easy for mechanical weathering to occur? (Lesson 5)

_____

_____

9. Describe the porosity and permeability of Antarctic soil. (Lesson 7)

_____

_____

10. How does Antarctic soil differ from soil found in warmer, wetter climates? (Lesson 8)

_____

_____

_____

Student Guide
Lesson 11: Unit Assessment

You have reached the end of the Earth's Surface unit. Take the Unit Assessment to complete the unit.

Lesson Objectives

- Describe the basic components of the Earth's physical systems: the atmosphere, biosphere, lithosphere, hydrosphere, and magnetosphere.
- Explain latitude and longitude and recognize them as providing a primary coordinate system for reference to places on the earth.
- Describe features on maps such as coordinate systems, scales, directional indicators, keys, symbols, and contour lines.
- Describe specific uses of topographic maps.
- Describe the major processes that break apart and move material around on the earth's surface to form soil from rock and organic material and to change the shape of the surface.
- Describe major agents of mechanical weathering and of chemical weathering, how the agents cause each kind of weathering, and how mechanical weathering and chemical weathering interact to enhance each other's effects.
- Describe major types of soil in terms of porosity, permeability, and climates in which they are found.

PREPARE

Approximate lesson time is 60 minutes.

ASSESS

Unit Assessment: Earth's Surface Unit Assessment, Part 1 (*Online*)

You will complete an online assessment of the main objectives covered so far in this unit. Follow the instructions online. Your assessment will be scored by the computer.

Unit Assessment: Earth's Surface Unit Assessment, Part 2 (*Offline*)

Complete the offline part of the Unit Assessment. Your learning coach will score this part of the Assessment.

Student Guide
Lesson 1: Identifying Minerals and Crystals

Think of the role that rocks play in our daily lives. Rocks are used to construct buildings and pave our roads. They contain many important natural resources, including oil, coal, iron, and salt. Look deeper into rocks, and you will see that almost all of them are made of minerals. In this unit, you will learn how to identify different rocks and minerals, explain how they form, and describe how they are used in everyday life.

If you could slice up a rock and place a very thin section under a microscope, you would see that it is actually made up of a lot of smaller pieces. These smaller pieces are minerals. Studying minerals helps us understand and classify rocks.

Lesson Objectives

- Describe how geologists classify rocks and minerals.
- Distinguish rocks from minerals.
- Give examples of observable properties used to identify minerals.

PREPARE

Approximate lesson time is 60 minutes.

Materials

> For the Student
>> 🖳 Mineral Crossword Puzzle

Keywords and Pronunciation

chemical properties : properties of a substance relating to the chemical nature and reactivity of a substance

cleavage (KLEE-vij) : the tendency of a mineral to split, when struck, along specific planes of the crystal structure

crystalline (KRIS-tuh-luhn) : made of crystal; containing a repeating structure of atoms

fracture (FRAK-chuhr) : breakage of a mineral, when struck, in a way that is not along cleavage planes of the crystal structure

hardness : the ability of a mineral to resist being scratched

luster : a description of a mineral based on how much light reflects off it

metallic (muh-TA-lik) : a description of the shiny luster of metals

mineral : a naturally occurring, inorganic substance with a specific chemical composition and crystal structure

opaque (oh-PAYK) : not transparent; light is unable to pass through

ore : a rock that contains a mineral that can be mined for profit

physical properties : properties of a substance that can be observed without changing the chemical makeup of the substance

silicate (SIH-luh-kayt) : any of a group of common minerals, such as quartz or feldspar, that make up 90 percent of the earth's crust

streak : a line of finely powdered mineral of characteristic color left when the mineral is rubbed across an unglazed porcelain tile

LEARN

Activity 1: Foundations *(Online)*

Activity 2: Minerals and Crystals *(Online)*

Activity 3: Mineral Crossword Puzzle *(Offline)*

A crossword puzzle provides a fun way for you to review terms and definitions related to the lesson. You will review key concepts by completing the crossword puzzle.

ASSESS

Lesson Assessment: Identifying Minerals and Crystals, Part 1 *(Online)*

You will complete an online assessment covering the main objectives of this lesson. Your assessment will be scored by the computer.

Lesson Assessment: Identifying Minerals and Crystals, Part 2 *(Offline)*

You will complete an offline assessment covering the main objectives of this lesson. Your learning coach will score this assessment.

Name _____   Date _____

Mineral Crossword Puzzle

Name _____   Date _____

Across

4.   Breakage of a mineral, when struck, in a way that is not along cleavage planes of the crystal structure.

7.   A characteristic of a mineral that is revealed by testing what substances can scratch it and what substances it can scratch.

8.   A line of finely powdered mineral of characteristic color left on an unglazed ceramic tile when the mineral is rubbed across it.

10.   The tendency of a mineral to split, when struck, along specific planes of the crystal structure.

Down

1.   A description of the appearance of a mineral with respect to how light is reflected off it.

2.   The ratio of the density of a mineral to the density of water is called specific_____.

3.   This characteristic varies according to which parts of the visible light spectrum are reflected from a mineral.

5.   Properties of minerals are determined by the arrangement of _____ , ions, or molecules held together in crystalline structures.

6.   A naturally occurring, inorganic solid substance with a fixed chemical composition and crystal structure.

9.   The three most abundant elements in the earth's crust are oxygen, silicon, and _____.

Name _____   Date _____

Identifying Minerals and Crystals, Part 2 Lesson Assessment

1. Using gabbro as an example, explain what makes gabbro a rock and not a mineral.

    _____

    _____

    _____

    _____

2. List the observable properties that scientists use to identify minerals. Explain why chemical properties are not always used to identify minerals.

    _____

    _____

    _____

    _____

    _____

    _____

Student Guide
Lesson 2: Lab: Mineral Identification

You have learned a lot about the basic building blocks on the earth's surface—minerals. Scientists can use several different traits to identify and organize minerals. Now you will have the opportunity to identify minerals on

your own.

Lesson Objectives

- Record scientific data using charts, graphs, and/or written descriptions.
- Identify minerals based on color, streak, hardness, and unique properties.
- Record scientific data using charts, graphs, and/or written descriptions.

PREPARE

Approximate lesson time is 60 minutes.

Advance Preparation

- You will need an eyedropper for this lesson. If you do not have an eyedropper, visit a local pharmacy and explain that you need one for a science project. They may be able to supply one free of charge. As an alternative, you may wish to use a regular drinking straw.

- The hardness test for minerals requires the use of a piece of glass. If glass is not available, the edge of a mirror will suffice. Please be aware, however, that some minerals may scratch the mirror and cause permanent damage to its surface.

Materials

For the Student

🖳 Data Table

🖳 Mineral Identification Lab

eyedropper

glass, piece

magnet

magnifying glass

nail, iron

penny

Rock and Mineral Kit

streak plate

vinegar, distilled white

Keywords and Pronunciation

cleavage (KLEE-vij) : the tendency of a mineral to split, when struck, along specific planes of the crystal structure

fracture (FRAK-chuhr) : breakage of a mineral, when struck, in a way that is not along cleavage planes of the crystal structure

luster : a description of a mineral based on how much light reflects off it

streak : a line of finely powdered mineral of characteristic color left when the mineral is rubbed across an unglazed porcelain tile

LEARN

Activity 1: Mineral Identification Lab *(Online)*

Minerals have many different properties that help scientists identify them. You have already read about these various traits. Now it's time to use what you know about mineral properties to identify unknown minerals.

In this lab, you will identify six mineral samples. You will identify one mineral by watching a video of the mineral being tested. Then, you will identify the other five minerals on your own. You will also view a video of the mineral samples being broken so you can observe cleavage and fracture on freshly broken surfaces without breaking your own samples.

After you print and gather your materials, begin your lab observations by watching the videos on the following screens.

Safety

Be careful while testing for hardness of the minerals, as it is possible to cut or scratch yourself with the iron nail and glass.

ASSESS

Lesson Assessment: Lab: Mineral Identification (*Online*)

Have an adult review your answers to the Mineral Identification Lab and input the results online.

Name _____ Date _____

Mineral Identification Lab Data Table

Sample Number	Color	Streak	Cleavage or Fracture	Hardness	Luster	Magnet Test: attracted?	Fizz Test: bubbles?
7							
13							
23							
25							
26							
27							

Name _____   Date _____

Mineral Identification Lab

Introduction

One of the most important scientific skills is observing. Being a good observer means more than noticing things with your eyes. Observing in science involves all of your senses.

When scientists work with minerals, they may use sight, touch, and even smell to determine the identity of a mineral sample. There are many properties that can be observed and used to identify minerals. Some properties you have studied are:

- color
- luster
- streak
- hardness
- cleavage

In this lab, you will practice making observations by investigating the properties of several mineral samples. Then you will identify each mineral based on your observations.

Hypothesis

Before you conduct a scientific test, you should think about what you predict will happen. Take a few minutes now to observe Samples 7, 13, 23, 25, and 27. Which sample or samples do you think will be hardest? Which sample or samples do you think will have a yellow streak?

Materials

Supplied

Rock and Mineral Kit

magnifying glass or hand lens

streak plate

magnet

Not Supplied

eyedropper

penny

nail

glass

white vinegar

 **Safety Stop**

Have you read the safety information for this lab activity? If not, return to the lesson and do so now.

Name   Date

Procedure

Watch the *Testing an Unknown Mineral* video to collect data for sample 26.

Observation 1: Color

Examine Sample 13 and observe its color. Record it in the Mineral Identification Data Table.

Observation 2: Streak

Scrape the sample across the streak plate and observe the color of its streak. Record the color in the data table.

Observation 3: Cleavage or Fracture

Observe the edges of the sample. Does the sample show cleavage, meaning that its edges are broken in flat planes? Or does it just show fracture, meaning that the edges are broken irregularly? Watch the *Breaking Minerals* video and then check your observations with those listed in the data table.

Observation 4: Hardness

The diagram below shows how some common materials compare in terms of hardness. Scientists use a numbered scale called the Mohs Hardness Scale to rate the hardness of minerals. Minerals range in hardness from 1 (talc) to 10 (diamond).

1	2	3	4	5	6	7	8	9	10
Talc	Fingernail	Copper penny	Iron nail	Glass	Streak plate	Quartz			Diamond

Start by trying to scratch the sample with your fingernail, and then move up to harder objects if you need to (you do not have to scratch the sample with a diamond). The sample will be scratched by objects with a higher hardness. The sample will scratch objects with a lower hardness.

How do you know if your sample has been scratched? After scratching, try to wipe the scratch away with your finger. If the scratch disappears, the sample was not actually scratched. Record the hardness in the data table.

Observation 5: Magnetism

Touch the sample with the magnet. Observe if it is attracted to the magnet.

Observation 6: Fizz Test

Use the eyedropper to carefully place a few drops of white vinegar on the sample. If any bubbles form, make a note of it in the column labeled fizz test in your data table.

Observation 7: Luster

Note if the mineral has metallic or nonmetallic luster.

Repeat Observations 1–7 for samples 7, 23, 25, and 27. Record your observations in the data table, and then complete the analysis section of the lab.

Name _____   Date _____

Analysis

Now you will use your observations to identify each mineral. Use the Mineral Identification Key below and your notes.

| | Mineral Identification Key | | | | | |
Mineral Name	Color	Streak	Cleavage or Fracture	Hardness	Luster	Special Properties
Graphite	Black	Iron black	Fracture	1–2	Metallic	Feels greasy, can mark paper
Magnetite	Black	Black	Fracture	6	Metallic	Magnetic
Hematite	Black or red	Red-brown	Fracture	1–6.5	Metallic	Magnetic
Galena	Lead-gray	Gray-black	Cleavage	2.5–3	Metallic	Heavy
Talc	White, gray, green	White	Cleavage	1	Nonmetallic	Feels greasy
Sulfur	Pale yellow	Pale yellow	Fracture	1.5–2.5	Nonmetallic	Rotten-egg odor
Halite	Colorless, red, white	White	Cleavage	2.5	Nonmetallic	None
Calcite	Any color, usually white	White	Cleavage	3	Nonmetallic	Fizzes in acids
Quartz	Clear, white, rose, violet, black	White	Fracture	7	Nonmetallic	None
Mica	Clear, brown, green, yellow	Yellow	Cleavage	2.5	Nonmetallic	None

Sample 7: _____

Sample 13: _____

Sample 23: _____

Sample 25: _____

Sample 26: _____

Sample 27: _____

Name _____ Date _____

Conclusion

1. Give two examples of minerals that have a property in common.

   _____

   _____

2. Could you have identified any of the minerals after having described only a few, rather than all, of the properties you tested? If so, give an example.

   _____

   _____

   _____

3. Why is it still a good idea to test more properties than might be necessary?

   _____

   _____

Name _____ Date _____

Lab: Mineral Identification Lesson Assessment

For the questions below, review your student's responses on the Mineral Identification Lab and input the results online.

1. Follow the procedures in the attached Mineral Identification Lab and, using the information gathered during the experiments, complete the Mineral Identification Lab Data Table.

2. Based on the data recorded in your Mineral Identification Lab Data Table, complete the **Analysis** section of the attached Mineral Identification Lab.

3. Based on the data you gathered during the experiment, answer the questions in the **Conclusion** section of the attached Mineral Identification Lab.

Student Guide
Lesson 3: Igneous Rocks

Step outside and stamp your foot on the ground. The earth seems very solid, doesn't it? But deep below the earth's surface, the temperature is so high that rocks actually melt. When this molten material cools, it turns solid and forms rocks. Scientists classify this type of rock as igneous rock.

Let's learn more about the types of igneous rocks and how they form. You might recognize some that you've encountered in your daily life.

Lesson Objectives

- Explain how igneous rocks are formed.
- Compare and contrast magma and lava.

PREPARE

Approximate lesson time is 60 minutes.

Materials

For the Student

    📖 Igneous Rock Cards

    markers or crayons

    Rock and Mineral Kit

    scissors

    websites listed in Unit Resources

    📖 Igneous Rocks Lesson Review

Keywords and Pronunciation

coarse-grained : having a rough texture

crust : the outermost, solid layer of any planet or moon

extrusive rock : fine-grained igneous rock that forms when lava cools quickly at the surface; also called volcanic rock

fine-grained : having a fine, smooth, even texture

igneous rock : rock formed by the cooling and solidification of hot liquid magma or lava

intrusive : coarse-grained igneous rock that cools slowly underground; also called plutonic rock

lava : molten rock or magma that emerges onto the earth's surface

magma : the molten or partly molten mixture of minerals, gases, and melted rock found below the earth's surface

texture : the size of individual mineral grains in rock

LEARN
Activity 1: Formed by Fire *(Online)*

Activity 2: Igneous Rock File *(Offline)*
Closely examine the igneous rocks in your Rock and Mineral Kit and begin keeping a record of your observations in a Rock File.

Activity 3: Igneous Rock *(Offline)*
Review what you have learned about igneous rocks. When finished, place your completed lesson review sheet in your Science Notebook.

ASSESS
Lesson Assessment: Igneous Rocks (*Online*)
You will complete an online assessment covering the main objectives of this lesson. Your assessment will be scored by the computer.

Name _____ Date _____

Igneous Rock Cards

By now you know that geologists can study rocks to find out how they were formed. Study some of the igneous rocks in your Rock and Mineral Kit and use the Unit Resources to fill out the "Special Features" section of the Igneous Rock Cards.

Cut out the cards and start your own Rock File. Use the blank rock file card to add information to your Rock File if you observe more rocks. You may even want to keep your rock records on the computer or start a Rockhound club by collecting rocks, minerals, or fossils in your area.

Materials

- granite (sample 6)
- basalt (sample 8)
- pumice (sample 17)
- rhyolite (sample 19)
- obsidian (sample 20)
- markers/crayons
- scissors
- websites found in Unit Resources

Granite

Contains: quartz, feldspar, mica

Where found / how formed: formed from magma, part of the earth's crust

Special features:

_____
_____
_____
_____
_____
_____
_____

Draw a picture of granite above.

Basalt

Contains: feldspar, pyroxene

Where found / how formed: formed from cooled lava, found in many locations on the earth – also found on the moon.

Special features:

_____
_____
_____
_____
_____
_____

Draw a picture of basalt above.

Pumice

Contains: silica, iron, magnesium

Where found / how formed: in areas with young volcanoes; largest producer is Italy; also found in Greece, Turkey, Chile, and the United States.

Special features:

_____

_____

_____

_____

_____

_____

_____

Draw a picture of pumice above.

Obsidian

Contains: iron and magnesium

Where found / how formed: near areas of volcanic activity

Special features:

_____

_____

_____

_____

_____

_____

_____

Draw a picture of obsidian above.

Rhyolite

Contains: quartz, feldspar

Where found / how formed: near areas of volcanic activity, including the United States

Special features:

_____
_____
_____
_____
_____
_____
_____

Draw a picture of rhyolite above.

_____

Contains:

_____

Where found / how formed:

_____
_____
_____

Special features:

_____
_____
_____
_____
_____
_____

Draw a picture of the rock above.

Name _____   Date _____

Igneous Rocks Lesson Review

Review what you have learned about igneous rocks. When finished, place your completed lesson review sheet in your Science Notebook.

Vocabulary Review

Read each sentence. Fill in the blanks with words from the Word Bank.

Word Bank

igneous   coarse   fine   magma   lava
iIntrusive   extrusive   molten   texture   cool

1. Rocks that cool within the earth's surface have rough or _____-grained textures.

2. _____ is a mixture of melted rock, gases, and minerals found below the earth's surface. Once it reaches the earth's surface, it is called _____.

3. Basalt is a rock that cooled quickly above the earth's surface; therefore its texture is _____-grained.

4. The scientific term for rocks that are formed below the earth's surface is_____. _____ describes rocks that are formed above the earth's surface.

5. Observing a rock's minerals and _____can give you clues about how it was formed.

6. Magma is made of melted or _____ material.

Short Answer

Read the information below. Write your answer after the question.

7. A geologist found two igneous rocks made of the same minerals. One is coarse-grained and the other is fine-grained. Explain how the textures of igneous rocks are related to how they are formed.

_____

_____

_____

_____

_____

Student Guide
Lesson 4: Sedimentary Rocks

Weathering and erosion from wind, running water, or ice create tiny pieces of rock that come together to form other rocks. In this lesson, you will learn how sedimentary rocks are formed and how they are classified.

Lesson Objectives

- Explain how sediment is formed.
- Describe the processes by which sediment becomes sedimentary rock.
- Describe features in sedimentary rocks that help geologists determine the environments in which the rocks formed.

PREPARE

Approximate lesson time is 60 minutes.

Materials

For the Student

📠 Sedimentary Rock Cards

hammer

markers or crayons

Rock and Mineral Kit

scissors

sock

websites listed in Unit Resources

📠 Sedimentary Rocks Lesson Review

Keywords and Pronunciation

cementation : the process of binding particles of rocks

clastic sedimentary rock : rock formed as a result of high pressure on rock fragments and other rocks

compaction : crushing or pressing

conglomerate (kuhn-GLAHM-ruht) : a sedimentary rock made up of large particles, such as pebbles and sand

coquina (koh-KEE-nuh) : soft porous limestone, made of fragments of shells and coral

fossil (FAH-suhl) : the remains of ancient living things

limestone : a common sedimentary rock consisting mostly of calcium carbonate

sandstone : a sedimentary rock formed by the compaction of sand and held together by a natural cement

sediment : loose rock fragments, grains of rock or sand, minerals, or shells and remains of small living things

sedimentary rock : rock formed when sediments are compressed and squeezed together

shale : rock composed of layers of claylike, fine-grained sediment

LEARN
Activity 1: Squeezing Sediment *(Online)*

Activity 2: Sedimentary Rock File *(Offline)*
Sedimentary rock features help geologists figure out where sedimentary rocks were formed. Examine sedimentary rocks in your Rock and Mineral Kit and add notes to your rock file.

Activity 3: Sedimentary Rocks *(Offline)*
Review what you have learned about sedimentary rocks. When finished, place your completed lesson review sheet in your Science Notebook.

ASSESS
Lesson Assessment: Sedimentary Rocks (*Online*)
You will complete an online assessment covering the main objectives of this lesson. Your assessment will be scored by the computer.

Name _____ Date _____

Sedimentary Rock Cards

How confident are you that you can "read" rocks? Try it by examining a few of the sedimentary rocks in your Rock and Mineral Kit. Then, complete the Special features section of the Sedimentary Rock Cards, cut them out, and add them to your Rock File. Use the blank file card to add information to your Rock File if you observe more rocks.

Want to see the crystals in your geode? Place the geode in a sock and hit it very lightly with a hammer. Your geode may not break perfectly in half, but you should be able to see crystals when it breaks into pieces.

Materials

- Sandstone (sample 5)
- Chert (sample 22)
- Mudstone (sample 31)
- Geode (sample 36)
- hammer
- sock
- markers/crayons
- scissors
- Websites from Unit Resources

Chert

Contains: fine quartz crystals and remains of ancient sea sponges and ocean animals

Where found/how formed: extremely rare, found near water

Special features:

_____
_____
_____
_____
_____
_____

Draw a picture of chert above.

Sandstone

Made of: quartz particles and sand grains

Where found/how formed: as layers in areas such as the Grand Canyon

Special features:

_____
_____
_____
_____
_____
_____

Draw a picture of sandstone above.

Mudstone

Made of: clay minerals, quartz, mica

Where found/how formed:
deep in the ocean or the bottom of a lake

Special features:

_____
_____
_____
_____
_____
_____
_____

Draw a picture of mudstone above.

Geode

Made of: rock, minerals calcite and quartz

Where found/how formed:
can form in any buried opening, including bubbles in igneous rocks, under tree roots, or even in animal burrows

Special features:

_____
_____
_____
_____
_____
_____
_____

Draw a picture of a geode above.

_____

Contains:

_____

Where found/how formed:

_____
_____
_____

Special features:

_____
_____
_____
_____
_____
_____
_____
_____

Draw a picture of the rock above.

Name _____   Date _____

Sedimentary Rocks Lesson Review

Review what you have learned about sedimentary rocks. When finished, place your completed lesson review sheet in your Science Notebook.

1. The sentences below about how sedimentary rocks are formed are not in order. Order them from 1-5 by placing the correct number in the blank next to the sentence.

    _____ Sediment settles into layers in water or on land.

    _____ Layers of sediment are compacted together by pressure.

    _____ Weathering breaks rock and other substances down into small particles called sediment.

    _____ Chemicals in water form a solid that cements sediment into sedimentary rock.

    _____ Erosion by wind, ice, or water transports sediment to a new location.

2. Match the feature listed below to the clues it provides about the environment in which sedimentary rocks are formed. Not all words are used.

    A. layers

    B. magma

    C. mud cracks

    D. fossils

    E. texture

    F. ripple marks

    _____ The rock may have been muddy at one time, but then dried.

    _____ Certain plants and animals once lived in the area.

    _____ Water may have moved very quickly through the area at one time.

    _____ A change in the environment may have occurred from one period of time to another.

Student Guide
Lesson 5: Metamorphic Rocks

Imagine rocks compressed down to a fraction of their original size, changing from one form to another. Evidence indicates it really happens, even though it takes a long time and can involve enormous forces and heat energy of the earth.

Lesson Objectives

- Explain how metamorphic rocks are formed.
- Give examples of metamorphic rocks and describe how they formed.

PREPARE

Approximate lesson time is 60 minutes.

Materials

For the Student

📇 Metamorphic Rock Cards

markers or crayons

Rock and Mineral Kit

scissors

websites listed in Unit Resources

📇 Lesson Review

Keywords and Pronunciation

foliated (FOH-lee-ay-tuhd) : relating to rock that has a layered structure

gneiss (niys) : foliated metamorphic rock, usually of the same composition as granite

marble : metamorphic rock formed by alteration of limestone, used especially in architecture and sculpture

metamorphic rock (meh-tuh-MOR-fik) : rock that has undergone change, caused by intense heat and pressure, from an earlier form, without melting

metamorphosis (meh-tuh-MOR-fuh-suhs) : change of physical form, structure, or substance

nonfoliated rock : metamorphic rock that does not separate into layers when broken

quartzite : metamorphic rock formed from quartz sandstone

schist (shist) : flaky metamorphic rock formed from clay and mud, composed of minerals such as mica, talc, hornblende, and graphite

slate : fine-grained metamorphic rock, formed from shale that splits into thin, smooth-surfaced layers

LEARN
Activity 1: Hard Pressed *(Online)*

Activity 2: Metamorphic Rock File *(Offline)*

Complete your Rock File by adding information about metamorphic rocks. Examine the metamorphic rocks in your Rock and Mineral Kit.

Activity 3: Metamorphic Rocks *(Offline)*

Review what you have learned about metamorphic rocks. When finished, place your completed lesson review sheet in your Science Notebook.

ASSESS

Lesson Assessment: Metamorphic Rocks (*Online*)

You will complete an online assessment covering the main objectives of this lesson. Your assessment will be scored by the computer.

Name _____ Date _____

Metamorphic Rock Cards

Complete your Rock File by adding information about metamorphic rocks to rock cards. Examine samples in your Rock and Mineral Kit. Then complete the Special features section of the metamorphic rock cards, cut them out, and add them to your Rock File. Use the blank file card to add information to your Rock File if you observe more rocks.

Materials

- gneiss (sample 2)
- slate (sample 4)
- marble (sample 9)
- quartzite (sample 29)
- markers/crayons
- scissors
- websites from Unit Resources

Gneiss

Contains: feldspar, mica, quartz (the same minerals as granite)

Where found/how formed: can be formed from sedimentary rock such as sandstone or shale or from igneous rock such as granite; can be found in Arizona

Special features:

_____

_____

_____

_____

_____

_____

Draw a picture of gneiss above.

Name _____ Date _____

Slate

Contains: quartz, muscovite, clay, volcanic ash

Where found/how formed: derived from shale that has undergone low pressure and temperatures; can be found in Pennsylvania, Vermont, and New York

Special features:

_____

_____

_____

_____

_____

Draw a picture of slate above.

Marble

Contains: calcite (which is also found in limestone)

Where found/how formed: metamorphosed from limestone or dolomite; can be found in Vermont, Tennessee, Missouri, Georgia, and Alabama

Special features:

_____

_____

_____

_____

_____

Draw a picture of marble above.

Name _____   Date _____

Quartzite

Contains: quartz, silica

Where found/how formed: heating of and pressure on sandstone; can be found in South Dakota, Minnesota, Arizona, and Utah

Special features:

_____

_____

_____

_____

_____

Draw a picture of quartzite above.

_____

Contains:

_____

Where found/how formed:

_____

_____

Special features:

_____

_____

_____

_____

_____

Draw a picture of the rock above.

Name _____   Date _____

Metamorphic Rocks Lesson Review

Review what you have learned about metamorphic rocks. When finished, place your completed lesson review sheet in your Science Notebook.

Vocabulary Crossword

Read each clue and fill in the puzzle with the term that is described.

Across

2. Rock that has changed form from heat and pressure

4. A type of metamorphic rock formed from limestone

5. Metamorphic rock that splits into sheets when broken

6. A mineral found in both limestone and marble

Down

1. Metamorphic rock that does not split into sheets when broken

3. A type of metamorphic rock formed from shale

Student Guide
Lesson 6. Optional: Your Choice

Lesson Objectives

- Practice skills and reinforce concepts taught in this course.

PREPARE

Approximate lesson time is 60 minutes.

Student Guide
Lesson 7: The Rock Cycle

It's hard to believe, but rocks are always changing. You may know that igneous and sedimentary rocks can turn into metamorphic rocks with heat and pressure. But did you know that a metamorphic rock can eventually become a sedimentary or igneous rock? Rocks are formed, moved, and transformed in the rock cycle.

Lesson Objectives

- Summarize how the earth's surface materials are constantly formed, reformed, and transformed from one type of rock into another through the processes of the rock cycle.
- Relate the rock cycle to the formation of layers of rock.
- Describe the arrangement of rocks in rock layers.

PREPARE

Approximate lesson time is 60 minutes.

Materials

For the Student

📖 All About Rocks

Keywords and Pronunciation

igneous rock : rock formed by the cooling and solidification of hot liquid magma or lava

metamorphic rock (meh-tuh-MOR-fik) : rock that has undergone change, caused by intense heat and pressure, from an earlier form, without melting

sediment : loose rock fragments, grains of rock or sand, minerals, or shells and remains of small living things

sedimentary rock : rock formed when sediments are compressed and squeezed together

LEARN
Activity 1: The Rock Cycle (Online)

Activity 2: All About Rocks (Online)

So you think you know all there is to know about rocks, right? Let's see how much you really know. Print the All About Rocks sheet and use the Word Bank to complete the passage.

ASSESS

Lesson Assessment: The Rock Cycle, Part 1 (*Online*)

You will complete an online assessment covering the main objectives of this lesson. Your assessment will be scored by the computer.

Lesson Assessment: The Rock Cycle, Part 2 (*Offline*)

You will complete an offline assessment covering the main objectives of this lesson. Your learning coach will score this assessment.

Name _____   Date _____

All About Rocks

Fill in each blank below with a term from the Word Bank. You will use each term once, and you will use all of the terms.

Word Bank

metamorphic rock	temperatures	rock cycle
sedimentary rock	thousands to millions	magma
igneous rock	weathering and erosion	

The series of pathways by which a rock may change from one type into another is called the _____. One part of the cycle includes the weathering and erosion of rocks into sediment. Sediment eventually forms _____ layers that may change into metamorphic or igneous rocks. For example, a sedimentary rock that undergoes high heat and high pressure may change into a _____. Even higher _____ lead to melting of rock and formation of _____. When magma cools, _____ is formed. _____ of sedimentary, igneous, and metamorphic rocks lead to the formation of sediment and, eventually, new sedimentary rocks. Due to the dynamic processes that occur on and below the earth's surface, it is common for rocks to change from one type into another. However, it takes _____ of years for these changes to occur.

Name _____ Date _____

The Rock Cycle, Part 2 Lesson Assessment

Use the lines provided to answer each question.

1. Describe how mudstone forms.

   _____

   _____

   _____

   _____

2. What are the main agents of change in the rock cycle?

   _____

3. Although it is rare, one type of rock can be changed into a different type of rock very quickly. Explain and give examples of how this could happen.

   _____

   _____

   _____

   _____

   _____

Student Guide
Lesson 8: Lab: Rock Cycle

You have already learned a great deal about rocks. But is it possible to learn from rocks? Indeed, it is! Much of what we currently know about the earth's past has been "told" to us by rocks. Because rocks are so old and cycle so slowly, they are one of the few records that scientists have of the geologic past. Now you will have a chance to learn from rocks!

Lesson Objectives
- Identify sources of information used in scientific research.
- Distinguish rocks from minerals.
- Give examples of observable properties used to identify minerals.

PREPARE

Approximate lesson time is 60 minutes.

Materials
   For the Student
      🖵 Rocks and the Rock Cycle
      Rock and Mineral Kit

LEARN
Activity 1: Review the Rock Cycle *(Online)*

Activity 2: Rocks and the Rock Cycle Lab *(Online)*
Scientists have found several different ways to "read" rocks to discover how they were formed and how they change. In this lab, you will experience and apply what you know about rocks to the rock cycle.

ASSESS
Lesson Assessment: Lab: Rock Cycle (*Online*)
Have an adult review your answers to the Rocks and the Rock Cycle Lab and input the results online.

Name _____   Date _____

Rocks and the Rock Cycle

The rock cycle explains what we know about how rocks form and change. It also helps scientists explain the appearance of rocks. In this activity, you will have a chance to actually place rocks in the rock cycle, make observations about the rocks, and draw conclusions about rock types. Use books, magazines, lessons, websites, or other scientific resources to find information to complete this lab.

Materials

construction paper

markers and/or crayons

gneiss, sample 2

slate, sample 4

sandstone, sample 5

granite, sample 6

basalt, sample 8

marble, sample 9

shale, sample 10

coquina, sample 11

conglomerate, sample 14

coal, sample 16

pumice, sample 17

limestone, sample 18

rhyolite, sample 19

obsidian, sample 20

diatomite, sample 21

chert, sample 22

graphite, sample 24

gabbro, sample 28

quartzite, sample 29

mudstone, sample 31

geode, sample 36

1. Using construction paper and colored pens, and referring to the rock cycle diagram online, create a rock cycle diagram showing each of the following:

    a. igneous rocks

    b. metamorphic rocks

    c. sedimentary rocks

    d. where erosion takes place

    e. where weathering takes place

    f. locations of volcanic activity

    g. where heat and pressure transform rocks

    h. where compaction and cementation occur

    i. other important phases in the rock cycle

2. Now that you have created your rock cycle diagram, take each rock (not mineral) and place it in the correct place in the rock cycle, sorting by rock type (sedimentary, igneous, metamorphic). Then, look at each group of rocks and complete the tables on pages 2 and 3.

Name _____   Date _____

3. Use books, websites, lessons, or other scientific resources to complete this table.

Name of Igneous Rock	Description of Rock	Possible Origin of Rock	Similar Characteristics with Rocks in this Group

Name of Metamorphic Rock	Description of Rock	Possible Origin of Rock	Similar Characteristics with Rocks in this Group

Name of Sedimentary Rock	Description of Rock	Possible Origin of Rock	Similar Characteristics with Rocks in this Group

Name _____   Date _____

Observations

4.   Complete the table to describe and compare rock types. Using your observations from the previous chart and your rock kit, compare and contrast the different types of rocks in the table below.

Rock Types	Igneous vs. Sedimentary	Metamorphic vs. Sedimentary	Metamorphic vs. Igneous
Comparison			

Analysis

5.   How would you describe the characteristics of each rock type? Which characteristics of one or more rocks in each group give clues about how that rock was formed?

_____

_____

Conclusions

6.   Choose one rock from your Rock and Mineral Kit. Write a brief history about the origins of this rock type using what you know about the rock cycle. Then, predict what might happen to this rock in the future.

_____

7.   List three sources of information (books, lessons, websites, magazines, etc.) used to conduct this investigation. Include titles, authors, and/or website addresses.

A. _____

B. _____

C. _____

Name _____   Date _____

Lab: Rock Cycle Lesson Assessment

For the questions below, review your student's responses on the Rocks and the Rock Cycle Lab and input the results online.

1. Follow the procedures in the attached Rocks and the Rock Cycle lab and, using the information gathered during the experiments, sort the rocks in your Rock and Mineral kit by type and complete the rock type tables.

2. Based on the information gathered during the experiment and the data recorded in the rock type tables, how would you describe the characteristics of each rock type? Which characteristics of one or more rocks in each group give clues about how that rock was formed?

3. Based on the information gathered during the experiment and the data recorded in the rock type tables, choose one rock from your Rock and Mineral Kit. Write a brief history about the origins of this rock type using what you know about the rock cycle. Then, predict what might happen to this rock in the future.

4. List three external sources of information (books, lessons, websites, magazines, etc.) used to conduct the Rocks and the Rock Cycle lab. Include titles, authors, and/or website addresses.

Name _____   Date _____

Rocks and the Rock Cycle

The rock cycle explains what we know about how rocks form and change. It also helps scientists explain the appearance of rocks. In this activity, you will have a chance to actually place rocks in the rock cycle, make observations about the rocks, and draw conclusions about rock types. Use books, magazines, lessons, websites, or other scientific resources to find information to complete this lab.

Materials

construction paper

markers and/or crayons

gneiss, sample 2

slate, sample 4

sandstone, sample 5

granite, sample 6

basalt, sample 8

marble, sample 9

shale, sample 10

coquina, sample 11

conglomerate, sample 14

coal, sample 16

pumice, sample 17

limestone, sample 18

rhyolite, sample 19

obsidian, sample 20

diatomite, sample 21

chert, sample 22

graphite, sample 24

gabbro, sample 28

quartzite, sample 29

mudstone, sample 31

geode, sample 36

1. Using construction paper and colored pens, and referring to the rock cycle diagram online, create a rock cycle diagram showing each of the following:

   a. igneous rocks

   b. metamorphic rocks

   c. sedimentary rocks

   d. where erosion takes place

   e. where weathering takes place

   f. locations of volcanic activity

   g. where heat and pressure transform rocks

   h. where compaction and cementation occur

   i. other important phases in the rock cycle

2. Now that you have created your rock cycle diagram, take each rock (not mineral) and place it in the correct place in the rock cycle, sorting by rock type (sedimentary, igneous, metamorphic). Then, look at each group of rocks and complete the tables on pages 2 and 3.

Name _____   Date _____

3.   Use books, websites, lessons, or other scientific resources to complete this table.

Name of Igneous Rock	Description of Rock	Possible Origin of Rock	Similar Characteristics with Rocks in this Group

Name of Metamorphic Rock	Description of Rock	Possible Origin of Rock	Similar Characteristics with Rocks in this Group

Name of Sedimentary Rock	Description of Rock	Possible Origin of Rock	Similar Characteristics with Rocks in this Group

Name _____ Date _____

Observations

4. Complete the table to describe and compare rock types. Using your observations from the previous chart and your rock kit, compare and contrast the different types of rocks in the table below.

Rock Types	Igneous vs. Sedimentary	Metamorphic vs. Sedimentary	Metamorphic vs. Igneous
Comparison			

Analysis

5. How would you describe the characteristics of each rock type? Which characteristics of one or more rocks in each group give clues about how that rock was formed?

_____

_____

Conclusions

6. Choose one rock from your Rock and Mineral Kit. Write a brief history about the origins of this rock type using what you know about the rock cycle. Then, predict what might happen to this rock in the future.

_____

7. List three sources of information (books, lessons, websites, magazines, etc.) used to conduct this investigation. Include titles, authors, and/or website addresses.

A. _____

B. _____

C. _____

Student Guide
Lesson 9: Unit Review

You have learned a great deal about rocks and minerals—how they form, how scientists classify them, and how changes in earth's lithosphere result in the continuous rock cycle. Do you remember what minerals are? How do sedimentary, igneous, and metamorphic rocks form? How are they different from one another? What can we learn about earth from rocks? Let's take another trip into the world of rocks and minerals.

Lesson Objectives

- Define rocks as composed of minerals and recognize that they are classified as igneous, sedimentary, or metamorphic based on how they were formed.
- Explain how sedimentary rocks are formed and identify features that help determine the type of environment in which they formed.
- Summarize the processes called the rock cycle.
- Explain how metamorphic rocks are formed.
- State the defining characteristics of a mineral.
- Recognize that physical and chemical properties of minerals are a result of the types and arrangements of their atoms.
- Explain how properties of minerals can be used in their identification.
- Explain how igneous rocks form and recognize how physical properties of an igneous rock reveal its origin.

PREPARE

Approximate lesson time is 60 minutes.

Materials

For the Student

🖳 Unit Review

LEARN
Activity 1: Rocks and Minerals *(Online)*

How much do you remember about rocks and minerals in the lessons that you have completed? Print the Unit Review and review previous lessons to answer the questions.

Name _____   Date _____

Rocks and Minerals Unit Review

Review important concepts about rocks and minerals by reviewing the lessons and activities you have completed in this unit. You will need to go back over parts of each lesson to complete the review. Read each question carefully, and then answer it in the space provided.

1. List the mineral properties you tested during the Mineral Identification Lab.

    _____

    _____

2. Which mineral from the Mineral Identification lab ranked highest in hardness?

    _____

3. Explain how the arrangements of atoms into crystalline structures help geologists identify minerals.

    _____

    _____

    _____

4. Name a mineral and describe three properties that can be used to identify it.

    _____

    _____

    _____

    _____

5. Review the igneous rock animation in the Igneous Rocks lesson. Explain how igneous rocks are formed from magma. Name one example each of an intrusive and extrusive igneous rock.

    _____

    _____

    _____

    _____

    _____

6. Review the sedimentary rock animation in the Sedimentary Rocks lesson. What two things need to happen to turn sediment into rock?

    _____

    _____

    _____

7. Review the metamorphic rock animation in the Metamorphic Rocks lesson. Describe how metamorphic rock can be formed from igneous, sedimentary, or other metamorphic rocks.

    _____

    _____

    _____

    _____

8. Review the rock cycle diagram in the Rock Cycle lesson and the Rock Cycle Lab. If you are unsure of any of the terms, make flashcards to review the processes involved in the rock cycle.

Student Guide
Lesson 10: Unit Assessment

Remember this gigantic rock? You now have a better understanding about how it may have been formed and what type of rock it is.

You have learned a lot about rocks and minerals. You are now ready to take the Unit Assessment.

Lesson Objectives

- Define rocks as composed of minerals and recognize that they are classified as igneous, sedimentary, or metamorphic based on how they were formed.
- Explain how metamorphic rocks are formed.
- State the defining characteristics of a mineral.
- Recognize that physical and chemical properties of minerals are a result of the types and arrangements of their atoms.
- Explain how properties of minerals can be used in their identification.
- Explain how igneous rocks form and recognize how physical properties of an igneous rock reveal its origin.
- Summarize the processes that are collectively known as the rock cycle.

PREPARE

Approximate lesson time is 60 minutes.

ASSESS

Unit Assessment: Rocks and Minerals, Part 1 (*Online*)

You will complete an online assessment of the main objectives covered so far in this unit. Follow the instructions online. Your assessment will be scored by the computer.

Unit Assessment: Rocks and Minerals, Part 2 (*Offline*)

Complete the offline part of the Unit Assessment. Your learning coach will score this part of the Assessment.

Student Guide
Lesson 1. Optional: Your Choice

Long before you were here, they were here: the many organisms that left traces of themselves in the earth. Study ancient fossils and learn what they can teach you about earth's past. Learn how to "read" the clues in the walls of the Grand Canyon and find out how scientists know that the desert lands of Arizona were once covered with warm, tropical oceans. The past is still with us today, if you know how to look for it.

Lesson Objectives

- Practice skills and reinforce concepts taught in this course.

PREPARE

Approximate lesson time is 60 minutes.

Student Guide
Lesson 2: Linking Past and Present

In July 1995, the Soufrière Hills volcano on the Caribbean island of Montserrat began to erupt. Within weeks, the nearby town of Plymouth was covered in a thick layer of volcanic ash. This recent volcanic eruption can teach us about earth's geologic history. Learn how two important geologists proposed that the present can be linked to the past.

Lesson Objectives

- Explain that the processes that have shaped the earth through geologic time are the same today as they were in the past.
- Summarize major findings of James Hutton and Charles Lyell.

PREPARE

Approximate lesson time is 60 minutes.

Materials

For the Student

🖳 Rates of Geologic Processes

Keywords and Pronunciation

erosion : the gradual removal of the surface of the land by water, wind, or glaciers

geology : the study of the earth: how it was formed, what it is made of, and how it changes over time; studying geology is like looking at the history of the earth

sediment : loose rock fragments, grains of rock or sand, minerals, or shells and remains of small living things

uniformitarianism (YOO-nuh-for-muh-TEHR-ee-uh-nih-zuhm) : a principle stating that the geological processes taking place on earth today are the same as those of the past and thus can be used to explain past geological events

uplift : the rise in elevation of a layer of rocks resulting from the application of forces within the earth

weathering : the breakdown of rocks by physical or chemical processes; weathering causes the rocks on a cliff to wear away

LEARN
Activity 1: Hutton, Lyell, and Uniformitarianism *(Online)*

Activity 2: Rates of Geologic Processes *(Offline)*

Activity 3: Linking Past and Present *(Offline)*

Lesson Review

Review what you have learned about the principle of uniformitarianism. When finished, place your completed lesson review sheet in your Science Notebook.

1. In your own words, define the principle of uniformitarianism.

_____

_____

_____

_____

_____

_____

_____

_____

2. How can an understanding of uniformitarianism help you to understand earth's past?

_____

_____

_____

_____

_____

_____

_____

_____

3. What did James Hutton conclude about geologic processes?

_____

_____

_____

_____

_____

_____

_____

4. Why did Hutton reason that the earth is very old?

_____

_____

_____

_____

_____
_____
_____
_____

5. How did Sir Charles Lyell contribute to modern geology?

_____
_____
_____
_____
_____
_____
_____
_____
_____
_____

ASSESS

Lesson Assessment: Linking Past and Present (*Online*)

You will complete an online assessment covering the main objectives of this lesson. Your assessment will be scored by the computer.

Name _____   Date _____

Rates of Geologic Processes

Hutton and Lyell's work was based on the idea that processes and forces that affect earth's surface have acted uniformly (in the same way) since earth formed. Mountains rise, valleys deepen, and sand grains collect now the same way they did long ago.

But earth has changed over time, and that could change the rates at which geologic processes such as erosion, deposition, and uplifting occur. The table below explains the average rate at which some geologic processes occur.

Process	Rate per 1,000 years	After 100,000 years	After 10,000,000 years
Sea level changes	10 m		
Regional erosion	2 m		
Uplift	10 cm		

1. Calculate the amount of sea level change, erosion, and uplift for 100,000 years and 10,000,000 years. Remember, 100 cm = 1 m.

   _____

2. After 10,000,000 years, how much of earth's surface would be eroded away?

   _____

3. After 10,000,000 years, how much uplift would occur?

   _____

4. Which is the fastest process: sea level changes, erosion, or uplift?

   _____

Need help? Have an adult check the teacher guide if you need help with your calculations.

Student Guide
Lesson 3: Earth's Age

On April 22 every year since 1970, the world celebrates Earth Day to honor the earth and renew our promise to keep it safe, clean, and healthy. By now, you know that the earth was here a long time before 1970—but how long? Find out how geologists use different techniques to determine the age of the earth.

Lesson Objectives

- Distinguish between absolute and relative dating techniques.
- Explain how geologists use radiometric dating to date rocks and fossils.
- Summarize geologic evidence for estimating the age of the earth.

PREPARE

Approximate lesson time is 60 minutes.

Advance Preparation

- Your student will need a shoebox or other box with a lid. The Rock and Mineral Kit box will work if you remove the sample tray.

Materials

For the Student

📖 Determining Half-Life

cubes, centimeter/gram

pen, felt-tip

shoebox with lid

Keywords and Pronunciation

absolute dating : a way of finding out the actual age of an object or event

fossil (FAH-suhl) : the remains of ancient living things

half-life : the time needed for half of a sample of radioactive material to decay

isotope (IY-suh-tohp) : one of two or more atoms of the same element that have the same number of protons but different numbers of neutrons

radiometric dating : a way of determining the approximate age in years of geologic samples using radioactive isotopes

relative dating : a way of finding out if one object or event is older or younger than another object or event

LEARN
Activity 1: A New Way to Date Earth *(Online)*

Activity 2: Working with Scientific Data: Determine Half-Life *(Offline)*

Activity 3: Earth's Age *(Offline)*
Lesson Review

Review what you have learned about relative age and absolute age. When finished, place your completed lesson review sheet in your Science Notebook.

True/False
Review the lesson to answer the questions below. Write "T" if the statement is true and "F" if the statement is false. Correct any false statements using the lines below each one. Some statements mention concepts you learned earlier in the unit.

1. _____Geologists estimate that the earth is about 4.6 billion years old.

_____

2. _____Relative dating methods are useful for figuring out the absolute age of geologic events.

_____

3. _____The principle of uniformitarianism was put forth in the 1700s.

_____

4. _____The absolute age of geologic events can never be determined.

_____

5. _____Radiocarbon dating methods cannot be used on materials older than about 60,000 years.

_____

6. _____Carbon-14 dating can be used to find the absolute age of teeth and pottery.

_____

7. _____Modern geologists no longer use relative dating methods, such as interpreting the sequence of rock layers.

_____

8. _____Rocks found on the moon indicate that the moon is older than the earth.

_____

_____

ASSESS

Lesson Assessment: Earth's Age, Part 1 *(Online)*
You will complete an online assessment covering the main objectives of this lesson. Your assessment will be scored by the computer.

Lesson Assessment: Earth's Age, Part 2 *(Offline)*
You will complete an offline assessment covering the main objectives of this lesson. Your learning coach will score this assessment.

Name _____   Date _____

Determining Half-Life

How do scientists figure out the age of rocks on earth? Let's take a look at some of their methods.

Relative Dating

Consider the following members of a family: Mother, Father, Grandmother, Son, and Daughter. It is impossible to figure out the exact age of any of the members of this family from just that information. You could draw some probable conclusions, however.

For example, Mother and Father are older than Son and Daughter. They are also likely to be younger than Grandmother. But that's about all you can say. This is an example of relative dating because the ages of the family members are relative but not exact. Relative dating works for rocks, too.

Scientists have recognized that layers of rock have been deposited in sequence, one on top of another. This leads them to conclude that rocks in the bottom layers of undisturbed rock are older than those in the top layers.

Absolute Dating

To find the absolute age of rocks, scientists use radiometric dating. Radiometric dating involves studying the amounts of radioactive isotopes in some material. Do the following activity to explore radiometric dating.

Materials

centimeter/gram cubes (100)

shoebox

felt-tip pen

Procedure

1. Imagine the centimeter gram cubes represent an imaginary element called Virtualium.

2. Mark only one side of each cube with a black marker or felt-tip pen.

3. Place all of the cubes in the box.

4. Hold the lid tightly and turn the box over twice. Remove the lid.

5. Take out all of the cubes that have the marked side up. These cubes represent atoms of Virtualium that have decayed.

6. In the data table, record the total number of cubes removed from the box (remember these are decayed) after each trial. Also record the total number of cubes left in the box.

7. Repeat steps 4 through 6 until you have completed 8 trials or until all of the cubes have been removed.

Data

Record your data in the table.

Data Table

Trial	Amount Decayed	Amount Left
1		
2		
3		
4		
5		
6		
7		
8		

Analysis

Use the information collected in your data table to make a graph. Label the horizontal (across) axis "Trials." Label the vertical (up and down) axis "Number of Atoms Remaining." Make a line graph to show the data in the "Amount Left" column of your Data Table.

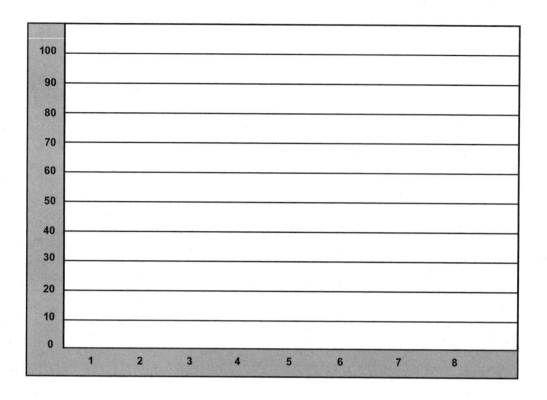

Conclusion

1. How many trials did it take for half of the Virtualium atoms to decay?

   _____

   _____

2. Suppose each trial equals 1,000 years. What is the half-life of Virtualium?

   _____

   _____

3. Suppose each trial equals 1,000 years. After half (50) of the Virtualium cubes were removed from the box, about how long did it take for half of the rest of the cubes to decay?

   _____

   _____

4. Imagine you have a radioactive sample containing both Virtualium and decayed atoms of Virtualium. After analysis, you find it contains 10 atoms of Virtualium and 40 decayed atoms. How old is your sample? (Hint: You must use the half-life of Virtualium determined earlier in the activity.)

   _____

   _____

Name _____   Date _____

Earth's Age, Part 2 Lesson Assessment

Answer the question below.

1. List and describe two pieces of evidence for scientists' ideas about the age of earth.

    _____

    _____

    _____

    _____

    _____

Student Guide
Lesson 4: Fossils

Why are fossils so important? Studying fossils can give us clues about what our planet was like millions of years ago. Fossils can tell what organisms existed and how they lived. Fossils give a record of the changes earth has experienced over time.

Lesson Objectives

- Describe fossils as recognized remains or traces of preexisting life, which may exist in the form of shells, bones, or impressions of plant leaves and soft body parts.
- Explain that fossils provide evidence of changes on earth over time.

PREPARE

Approximate lesson time is 60 minutes.

Keywords and Pronunciation

body fossil : the remains of a dead organism's actual body parts

excavate : to remove from the ground by digging

fossil (FAH-suhl) : the remains of ancient living things

index fossil : a fossil found to be especially useful in correlating rock layers across large distances

paleontologist (pay-lee-ahn-TAH-luh-jist) : a scientist who studies the history of life on earth as shown in fossils

trace fossil : a fossil formed from the footprints, burrows, or other activities of a living organism

tyrannosaurus (tuh-RAN-uh-SAWR-us) : a large, carnivorous dinosaur

LEARN
Activity 1: Finding Out from Fossils *(Online)*

Activity 2: Environments of Long Ago *(Offline)*
Antarctic Fossils

It was once thought that Antarctica was always an icy "wasteland." However, today scientists think that Antarctica had a very different environment millions of years ago. What do you know about present-day Antarctica? Consider the following:

- Antarctica is not welcoming to life.
- It has an ice cap about 4,000 meters (13,000 feet) thick.
- Antarctica has a month of complete darkness every year.
- During the summer, the sun shines up to 24 hours a day.
- Land mammals cannot survive in Antarctica.
- Blizzards of loose snow occur often.
- Antarctica is a barren, frozen wasteland.
- Antarctica includes the South Pole and is not connected to other continents.

What was Antarctica's paleoenvironment, that is, the environment millions of years ago, like? Below are some facts about fossils found in Antarctica. Sort out the key information that will help you figure out what Antarctica was like in the past. Then answer the questions.

Fossils Found in Antarctica Provide Clues to Its Paleoenvironment

- About 110 million years ago, labyrinthodonts, a group of extinct amphibians, lived in the river valleys of the ancient continent Gondwana and the rift valley that existed at that time between Australia and Antarctica.
- In March 1968, a fossilized jawbone of a labyrinthodont was found in central Antarctica.
- In 1986, fossils of a duck-billed dinosaur were found in Antarctica, along with remains of Antarctica's most ancient bird and many giant marine reptiles.
- Fossil bones of a land reptile, lystrosaurus, which lived in Antarctica about 200 million years ago, have been found in sandstones deposited by ancient rivers. Fossil remains of ancient ferns from the same period were also found.
- British geologists have discovered evidence of great fossil forests in Antarctica matching forests that grew on the Pacific Coast of the United States 20 million years ago.
- Duck-billed dinosaur fossils had only been found in either North or South America before one was found in Antarctica.
- Coal is formed from fossilized plants. The tooth of a duck-billed dinosaur was found in sands about 66–67 million years old.
- The tooth fossil indicated that the duck-billed dinosaur was a plant eater.
- Geologists at Ohio State University have found tree stems, roots, pollen, and tiny fossils of open-water marine life from the Pliocene period (2–4 million years ago).
- Labyrinthodonts survived in hot or warm climates.
- Sir Ernest Shackleton found coal beds within 200 miles of the South Pole in Antarctica.
- In 1952, Dr. Lyman H. Dougherty found two species of tree fern called Glossopteris that was once common in Africa, South America, and Australia. He also found a fossil footprint of a mammal-like reptile.
- In 1929, Admiral Byrd discovered mountains in Antarctica made of sedimentary rock. The rocks of the Edsel Ford Mountains were probably formed from sediment that collected after being carried by water.

Organize the Facts

1. Which lived in Antarctica earlier: the labyrinthodont, lystrosaurus, or duck-billed dinosaur? Explain.

_____

_____

_____

2. How could the duck-billed dinosaur tooth fossil lead scientists to believe that plants also existed in Antarctica?

_____

_____

_____

3. List three other types of evidence that plants existed in Antarctica.

_____

_____

_____

4. What was Antarctica's climate like millions of years ago? Provide two types of evidence.

_____

_____

_____

5. Did flowing water exist on Antarctica in the distant past? How do you know?

_____

_____

_____

6. Do you think ancient Antarctica was situated in a different location from its location today? Why or why not?

_____

_____

_____

7. Imagine you visited Antarctica 66 million years ago. Draw a scene you might have witnessed on your trip. Include any plant or animal life you might have been likely to see.

ASSESS

Lesson Assessment: Fossils (*Offline*)

You will complete an offline assessment covering the main objectives of this lesson. Your learning coach will score this assessment.

Name _____   Date _____

Fossils Lesson Assessment

Short Answer

Answer each question in the space provided.

(5 pts.)

1.   Give an example of a body fossil.

   _____

   _____

(5 pts.)

2.   Give an example of a trace fossil.

   _____

   _____

(10 pts.)

3.   Why would a leaf be preserved only as an impression?

   _____

   _____

(10 pts.)

4.   Study the diagram below. What do the two types of fossils found in these two rock layers tell you about the changes in the environment in this area over time?

   _____

   _____

Student Guide
Lesson 5: Records in Rocks

Why do we study rock layers? Rock layers help us learn about the history of earth. Each layer of rock tells a story about the area and records changes on earth's surface over time. In this lesson, you will learn how rocks tell the story of earth's past.

Lesson Objectives

- Explain how scientists use rock layers to gain information about earth's geologic past.

PREPARE

Approximate lesson time is 60 minutes.

Materials

> For the Student
>> 🖳 Rock Record

Keywords and Pronunciation

brachiopod (BRAY-kee-uh-pahd)

unconformity (uhn-kuhn-FAWR-muh-tee) : a gap in the rock record that indicated a time where *no* deposition has occurred, or where erosion *has* taken place

LEARN
Activity 1: Rock Layers Revealed *(Online)*

Activity 2: Rock Record *(Offline)*
As you know, sedimentary rocks are laid down when other rocks are eroded and the debris is deposited, often in layers. By observing sedimentary rock layers, geologists can determine events that took place and in what order they occurred. This is called a rock record.

To complete the activity, refer to the rules for studying sedimentary rock layers that you wrote in your Science Notebook earlier in this lesson.

ASSESS

Lesson Assessment: Records in Rocks, Part 1 (*Online*)
You will complete an online assessment covering the main objectives of this lesson. Your assessment will be scored by the computer.

Lesson Assessment: Records in Rocks, Part 2 (*Offline*)
You will complete an offline assessment covering the main objectives of this lesson. Your learning coach will score this assessment.

Name   Date

Rock Record

Record A.

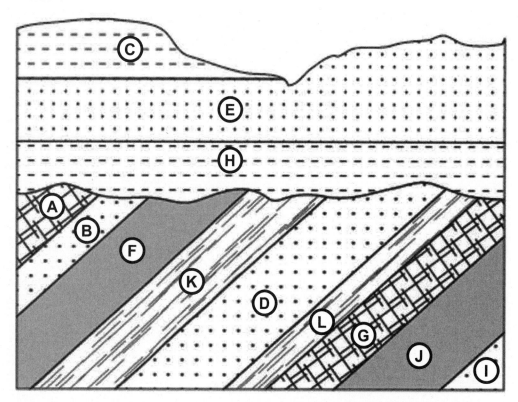

Record B.

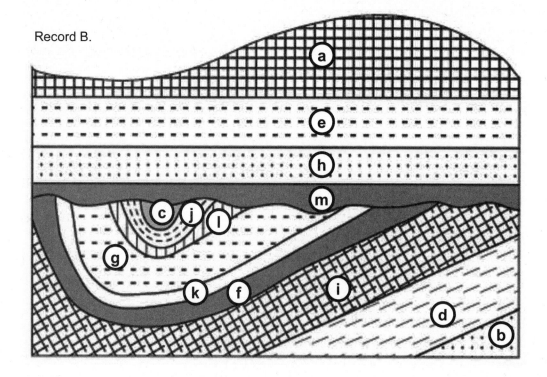

Name _____   Date _____

Use the Rock Record on page 1 to complete the questions below.

1. Examine Record A. Use the three basic rules to figure out the ages of the layers. In Chart A, list the layers from youngest to oldest, with the youngest layer in the first row.

2. Look for signs of tilting, erosion, or folding. In the second column in Chart A, write whether you think tilting, erosion, or folding took place. Write "tilting," "erosion," or "folding" next to the letter of any rock layer that was formed when the tilting, erosion, or folding took place. If you see no evidence of tilting, erosion, or folding, write "none."

3. Repeat steps 1 and 2 for Record B. Record the data in Chart B.

Data

Chart A	
Rock Layers (youngest to oldest)	**Tilting, Erosion, or Folding**
1	
2	
3	
4	
5	
6	
7	
8	
9	
10	
11	
12	

Name _____   Date _____

Chart B	
Rock Layers (youngest to oldest)	**Tilting, Erosion, or Folding**
1	
2	
3	
4	
5	
6	
7	
8	
9	
10	
11	
12	
13	

Observations

1.   Where does the unconformity occur in Record A and Record B?

_____

Name _____   Date _____

Analysis

2.   Study Record A. What can you say about the age of layer *K* from your data
     and observations?

     _____

3.   Study Record B. What can you say about the age of layer *c* from your data
     and observations?

     _____

4.   What do you think took place in layers C and E, exposed at the top surface of the layers in
     record A?

     _____

Conclusions

5.   Write about how the group of rock layers in Record A formed. Include tilting, erosion,
     and folding.

     _____

     _____

     _____

     _____

6.   Write about how the group of rock layers in Record B formed. Include tilting, erosion,
     and folding.

     _____

     _____

     _____

     _____

Name _____   Date _____

Record in Rocks, Part 2 Lesson Assessment

Use the diagram below to answer questions 1, 2, and 3.

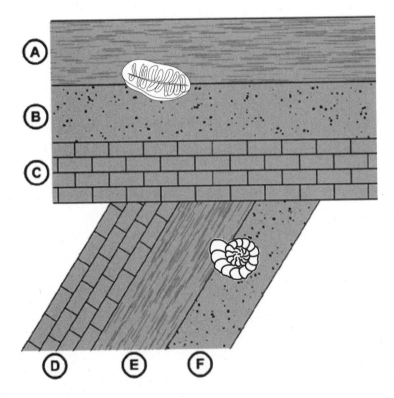

1. There is evidence of an unconformity between which two layers?

    _____

2. In searching rock layers for fossils, you make an interesting discovery. In layer F, you find fossilized clam shells. In layer B, you find fossilized leaf and tree impressions. What would you say about the environment where these layers were deposited?

    _____

    _____

3. Which existed first, the clam or the leaf? Why?

    _____

    _____

Student Guide
Lesson 6: Lab: Index Fossils and Paleoenvironments

Geologists find excitement in locating and describing new fossils. These fossils not only tell about life in the past, but they can also be used to understand the rock layers in which they were found. Besides, the type of rock in which a fossil is found can give a clue as to the environment in which the organism lived.

Use fossils to match rock layers in two different places on earth and then find out what clues fossils provide to understanding environments of the past.

Lesson Objectives

- Investigate how fossil patterns in rock layers provide information about earth's geologic past.

PREPARE

Approximate lesson time is 60 minutes.

Materials

For the Student

    🖳 Rock Layers and Index Fossils

    pencils, colored 12

Keywords and Pronunciation

index fossil : a fossil found to be especially useful in correlating rock layers across large distances

paleobotany (PAY-lee-oh-BAH-tuh-nee)

paleoenvironment (PAY-lee-oh-in-VIH-ruhn-muhnt)

strata : stratum (plural, strata): a single sedimentary rock unit with a distinct set of mineralogical characteristics or fossils that allow the layer to be easily distinguished from the rocky layers above and below it

LEARN
Activity 1: Pre-Lab: Index Fossils (Online)

Activity 2: Index Fossils and Paleoenvironments (Offline)
Rock Layers Revealed

Index fossils can be used to match up or correlate rock layers, or strata. Geologists continue to figure out the timeline of fossils by studying fossils in strata all over the world. They keep two important things in mind while studying strata.

1. Sedimentary rock layers are deposited one on top of another in horizontal layers. The oldest layer is at the bottom of the stack and the youngest is at the top.
2. Often species appear at a certain time and then become extinct at a later time. Once a species becomes extinct, it never appears again. An index fossil is one that occurs only during a specific geologic time and can be used to identify the rock layer it is found in.

Correlating Layers

Look closely at the Rock Layers and Index Fossils sheet. Notice the rock layers in Figure 1, which are identified by letters. Here you see two columns of rock layers, one in Idaho and one in Spain. You can see a fossil in layer "d."

1. Make a prediction about which layers in Idaho match layers in Spain by lightly drawing connecting lines in pencil between the layers.

2. Which layer in Spain do you predict will contain a dinosaur bone like the one in layer "d" in Idaho? Write your answer in the Hypothesis section below.

3. Study Figure 2, which shows known index fossils and in which layer they are found. Each index fossil will be found in only one layer in Idaho and only one layer in Spain.

4. Draw the fossils shown on the chart into the layers in Figure 1. For example, index fossil 2 should be drawn only in layers "c" and "i." Draw only one fossil in each layer. The drawings will help you match the layers.

5. Check your prediction. Use a different colored pencil to connect the layers in Idaho to the layers in Spain using the fossil evidence you just drew.

Hypothesis

Which layer in Spain will have a fossil matching the one found in Idaho?

_____

Analysis

Use your data to answer the question: Which layer in Spain could contain a dinosaur fossil like the one found in Idaho?

_____

Conclusion

1. Check your original prediction, or hypothesis about how the layers were correlated. Did you predict the correct layer that would have the dinosaur fossil? Explain whether your prediction was correct. Tell what clue made the biggest difference.

_____
_____
_____

2. How would you use your results to tell the relative ages of the rock layers in a new section of strata?

_____
_____
_____

3. In your own words, explain why you think that geologists find relative dating useful.

_____
_____
_____
_____

ASSESS

Lesson Assessment: Lab: Index Fossils and Paleoenvironments (*Online*)

Have an adult review your answers to the Index Fossils and Paleoenvironments Lab and input the results online.

Name _____   Date _____

Rock Layers Revealed

Figure 1: Rock Layers

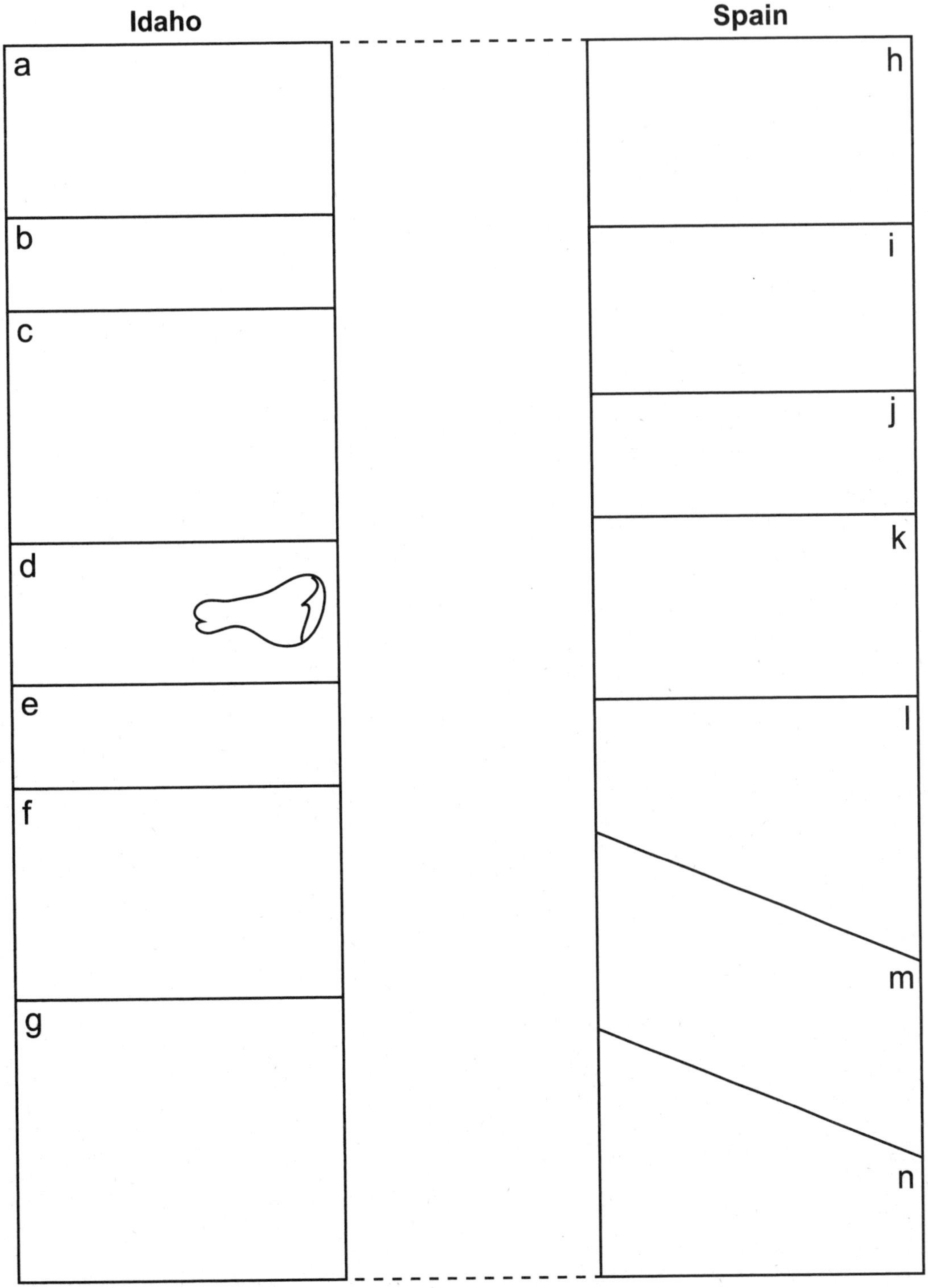

Name _____   Date _____

1.

2.

3.

4.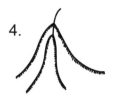

5.

6.

7.

8.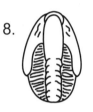

Figure 2: Index Fossils and Layers
Where They Are Found

Index Fossil Number	Found in Layer Letter (s)
1	b, h
2	c, i
3	l
4	f, m
5	e, k
6	a
7	d, j
8	g, n

Name _____   Date _____

Lab: Index Fossils and Paleoenvironments Lesson Assessment

For the questions below, review your student's responses on the Index Fossils and Paleoenvironments Lab and input the results online.

1. Follow the procedures in the attached Student Guide, complete the Rock Layers Revealed activity sheet.

2. Based on the data gathered in the Rock Layers and Index Fossils activity sheet, which layer in Spain could contain a dinosaur fossil like the one found in Idaho?

3. Based on the data gathered in the Rock Layers and Index Fossils activity sheet, how would you use your results to tell the relative ages of the rock layers in a new section of strata?

Name _____   Date _____

Rock Layers Revealed

Figure 1: Rock Layers

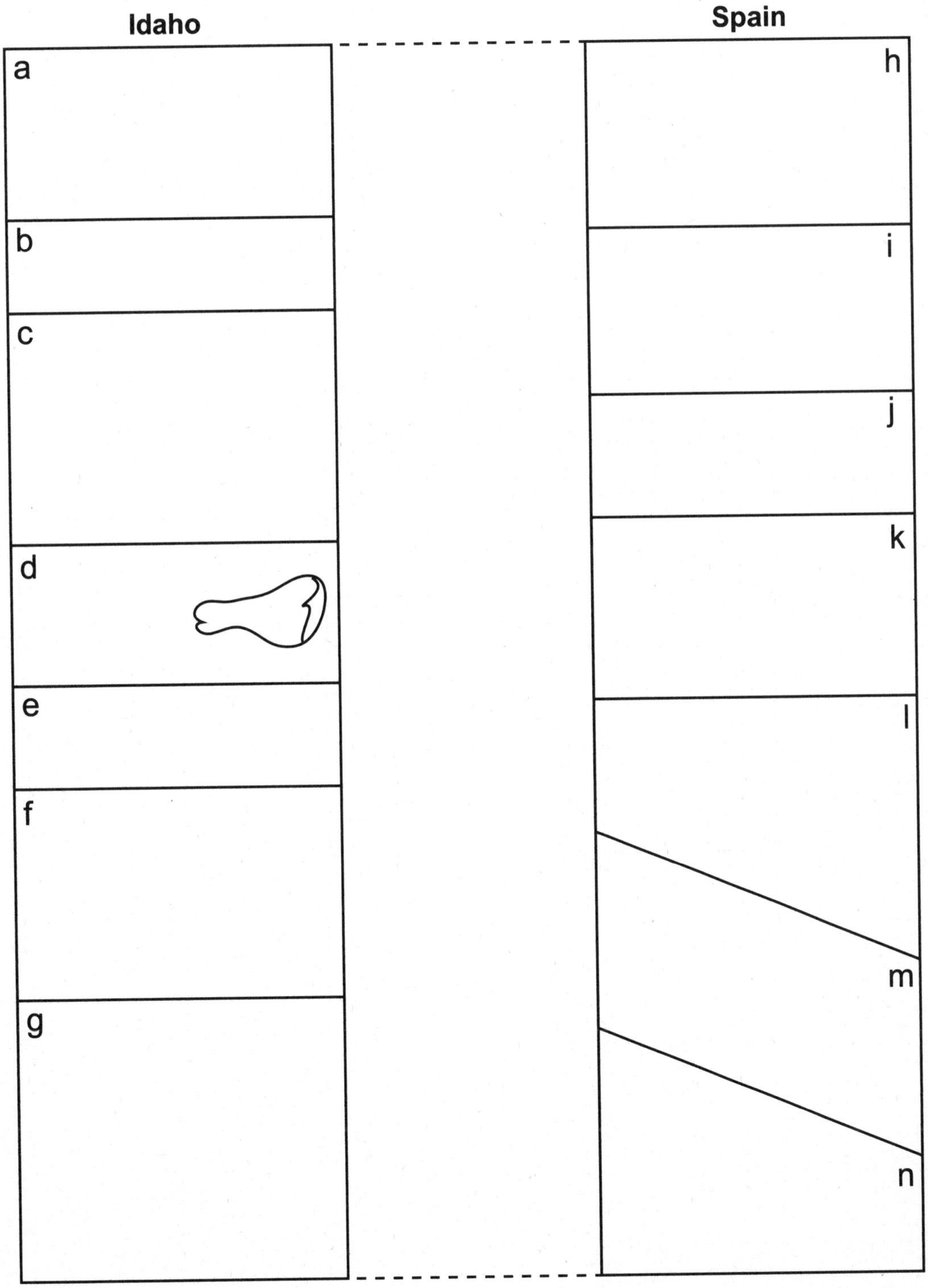

Name _____   Date _____

1.

2.

3.

4.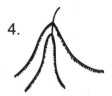

5.

6.

7.

8.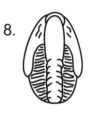

Figure 2: Index Fossils and Layers
Where They Are Found

Index Fossil Number	Found in Layer Letter (s)
1	b, h
2	c, i
3	l
4	f, m
5	e, k
6	a
7	d, j
8	g, n

Student Guide
Lesson 7: A Journey Through Geologic Time

Events in your life can be grouped together into certain periods of time. "Infant," "Toddler," and "Child" are a few you have lived through. Soon you may add "Teenager" and then "Adult." Just as you can divide your life into stages, geologists organize earth's history into different time periods. Each segment of time is based on important changes in the physical features or organisms on earth. Let's explore earth's history by studying a geologic timeline.

Lesson Objectives

- Interpret a diagram of geologic time scale, including eons, eras, periods, and the approximate time frame for these events.

PREPARE

Approximate lesson time is 60 minutes.

Advance Preparation

- This lesson presents information consistent with the general scientific consensus about the age of the earth.

Materials

For the Student

- Exploring Geologic Time
- Geologic Time in a Year

Keywords and Pronunciation

Cambrian (KAM-bree-uhn)

Carboniferous (KAHR-buh-NIH-fuh-ruhs)

Cenozoic (see-nuh-ZOH-ihk)

Cretaceous (kree-TAY-shuhs)

Devonian (dih-VO-nee-uhn)

eon (EE-ahn) : the longest period of geologic time

epoch (EH-puhk) : a subdivision of a period in geologic time

era : the longest unit of time on the geologic time scale (Do not confuse it with the word *eon*, which is a term indicating time longer than an era.)

extinction : the dying out of a species so that no members exist

Jurassic (juh-RA-sihk)

Mesozoic (meh-zuh-ZOH-ihk)

Ordovician (OR-duh-VI-shuhn)

Paleozoic (pay-lee-uh-ZOH-ihk)

period : a subdivision of an era in geological time

Permian (PUHR-mee-uhn)

Precambrian (pree-KAM-bree-uhn)

Quaternary (kwuh-TUHR-nair-ee)

Silurian (sih-LOUR-ee-uhn)

Tertiary (TUHR-shi-air-ee)
Triassic (triy-A-sihk)

LEARN

Activity 1: Understanding Geologic Time *(Online)*

Print the activity sheet, Exploring Geologic Time. You will use it after you read the next few screens.

Activity 2: Geologic Time in a Year *(Offline)*

It took nearly 4.6 billion years for life on earth to become what it is today. That is a long time! The following activity will help you understand how long, and just how short a time human life has been a part of earth's history.

ASSESS

Lesson Assessment: A Journey Through Geologic Time, Part 1 *(Online)*

You will complete an online assessment covering the main objectives of this lesson. Your assessment will be scored by the computer.

Lesson Assessment: A Journey Through Geologic Time, Part 2 *(Offline)*

You will complete an offline assessment covering the main objectives of this lesson. Your learning coach will score this assessment.

Name _____   Date _____

Exploring Geologic Time

Directions

Use the Geologic Timeline to answer the questions below. Then, use the numbered letters to answer the question at the bottom of the page.

1. What is the name of the current eon in which we live?

2. What event ended the Paleozoic and Mesozoic eras?

3. During which era did dinosaurs become extinct?

4. During which period did the supercontinent Pangaea form?

5. How many times did earth experience periods of global warming?

6. Which began forming during the Ediacaran period; the Appalachian Mountains or the Rocky Mountains?

7. The appearance of what element on earth allowed life to flourish?

8. What is the name of the first supercontinent to form?

9. Which era had the greatest amount and variety of mammal life?

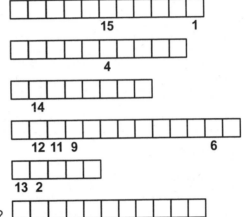

Evidence indicates that 65 million years ago, a giant meteorite crashed into earth, causing this landform as a result.

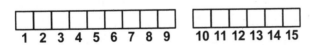

Think About It: What do you notice about climate of the Eocene epoch, Cretaceous period, and the Cryogenian period and the appearance of plants and animals?

_____

_____

_____

_____

Name _____   Date _____

Geologic Time in a Year

Directions

Below are some events in earth's history. Imagine that geologic time is compressed to the space of one calendar year. At this scale, 1 day equals about 12,602,740 years! When would the events below occur if we could compress geologic time in this way? There are a few hints to help you. You should guess the date but do not have to guess the exact time. Some of the data for this activity has been provided by the Kentucky Geological Survey, a research center of the University of Kentucky.

Years ago	Time	Event	Date if time was compressed to a calendar year
4.6 bya	Precambrian	Beginning of earth	1/1/00 12:00 AM
3.8 bya	Precambrian	Oldest age-dated rocks on earth	3/5/00 11:28 AM
1.5 bya	Ectasian Period	First multicelled organisms (seaweed and algae)	
505 mya	Cambrian Period	First fish	11/21/00 10:18 PM
470 mya	Silurian Period	First fossil evidence of land plants	
385 mya	Devonian Period	First insects (beetles, scorpions, centipedes)	
375 mya	Devonian Period	First land animals	12/2/00 5:52 AM
370 mya	Devonian Period	First sharks	12/2/00 3:23 PM
365 mya	Carboniferous Period	First seed plants	
228 mya	Triassic Period	First small dinosaurs	12/13/00 9:48 PM
115 mya	Cretaceous period	First flowering plants	
70 mya	Cretaceous Period	Tyrannosaurus Rex and Velociraptor	12/26/00 10:41 AM
64 mya	Paleocene Epoch	First ancestors of dogs and cats	
55 mya	Eocene Epoch	First horses	12/27/00 3:15 PM
39 mya	Eocene Epoch	First monkeys	
4 mya	Pliocene	First human-like ancestors	12/31/00 5:20 PM
0.1 mya	Recent Epoch	First modern man	

Name _____ Date _____

A Journey Through Geologic Time Lesson Assessment

Directions

Read the question carefully and answer on the lines provided.

1. Geologic time is divided into segments based on two kinds of information. What are they?

    _____

    _____

    _____

2. Describe the climate, landforms, and existing plant and animal life during the Cretaceous Period.

    _____

    _____

    _____

Student Guide
Lesson 8: Unit Review

Rock layers, dating methods, fossils...in this unit you have learned how these have contributed to learning about earth's past. This has earned you a place on the La Brea Tar Pits Pit 91 excavation team. Prepare for the unit assessment with a visit to the tar pits, a place where geologists use these same tools to learn about earth over 10,000 years ago.

Lesson Objectives

- Recognize the principle of uniformitarianism and its importance in determining historical events based on geological information.
- Recognize how fossils can be interpreted as evidence of preexisting life.
- Recognize and explain methods by which scientists determine the sequence of geological events, and the life forms and environmental conditions that existed in past geologic eras.
- Describe the geologic time scale and provide examples of major geological and biological events of each era.
- Recognize the major historic contributions to interpreting sedimentary rock layers made by James Hutton and Charles Lyell.

PREPARE

Approximate lesson time is 60 minutes.

Materials

For the Student

⌨ Geologic Map of California

LEARN
Activity 1: Prepare for the La Brea Tar Pits (Online)

Activity 2: A Visit to Rancho La Brea (Online)
Instructions

Unit Review
Your visit to the La Brea Tar Pits will help you review concepts you have learned in this unit. Read the information carefully and refer back to earlier lessons to answer the questions.

Background
Welcome to the Rancho La Brea Tar Pits, a hotbed of fossil digging activity, located in Los Angeles, California. The La Brea Tar Pits hold one of the richest fossil deposits. Here, tar formed from oil seeping through rock, trapped and preserved more than three million fossils in good condition. "Brea" actually means "tar" in Spanish. The fossils tell about life in the Los Angeles Basin 28,000 years ago.

1. Review the Geologic Time scale in Lesson 7 of this unit. What era, period, and epoch occurred 28,000 years ago?

Era:_____

Period:_____

Epoch:_____

2. What fossils would you expect to find at La Brea Tar Pits?

_____

Pit 91

Of the more than 100 tar pits at Rancho La Brea, only pit 91 continues to be excavated each summer. Volunteers who spend time working in the fossil laboratory at Rancho La Brea are allowed to sign up to help in pit 91. In the fossil laboratory, you can see fossils cleaned, labeled, and registered.

Geology

Study the geologic map to see the various types of rock found in California. The La Brea Tar Pits are located in the southwest corner of California near the Transverse Ranges and San Gabriel Fault.

3. Label the La Brea Tar Pits on your map.

4. From which era are the oldest rocks found in California? _____

5. What dating method was probably used to find the exact age of these rocks? _____

Let's dig

Most often, paleontologists must do a lot of work to find and uncover a fossil. They must also do research to figure out where to dig. If they are looking for a particular fossil, they must know how old the rocks are in the area. If they are looking for a land animal fossil, they will not want to look at rocks that were likely underwater at the time.

6. Review the steps of how a fossil is formed in Lesson 4. Why is the rock around Rancho La Brea better for finding fossils than the area in the Sierra Nevada mountains?

_____

_____

_____

7. If you were looking for a saber-toothed cat fossil, why would the rock around Rancho La Brea more likely contain this fossil than the rock in the Coastal Ranges? You may want to refer to Lessons 3, 4, and 7 of this unit. _____

_____

_____

Findings at Rancho La Brea

The La Brea Tar Pits are called a fossil hotbed for good reason; each summer thousands of fossils are found. Here are some of the fossils found there:

350 wolf bones including 3 skulls (2005)

327 saber-tooth cat bones including 5 skulls (2005)

150 bird fossils (2005)

Bison fossils (2003)

Horse fossils (2003)

Plant remains (2003)

Rabbit ankle bone (2001)

90 plant fossils (2000)

55 wood fossils (1998)

Coyote bones (1998)

8. The fossils in the list above are examples of which type of fossil? _____

9. Sometimes, rodent teeth marks are found in fossil bones. Rodents fed on animal remains at the surface. Which type of fossil is this an example of? _____

10. Why were there no dinosaur fossils found at La Brea? _____

_____

Rancho La Brea Long Ago

Studies of the fossils at Rancho La Brea show that horses, bison, and camels were eating a type of grass that no longer grows in the area because it depends on summer rain.

11. What does this tell you about how Rancho La Brea's climate was like long ago?

_____

12. Based on your answer to number 11, what must its climate be like now?

_____

La Brea Today

Today, the La Brea Tar Pits are a wonderful place to visit to learn about the past. You may be able to visit La Brea one day, but if not you can easily take a virtual tour. By visiting the La Brea Tar Pits website in your Unit Resources, you can learn about La Brea geology, animals and plants, and exploration and excavations. The Pleistocene is just a few clicks away.

Student Guide
Lesson 9: Unit Assessment

You have reached the end of the Geologic History unit. Take the Unit Assessment to complete the unit.

Lesson Objectives

- Recognize the principle of uniformitarianism and its importance in determining historical events based on geological information.
- Recognize how fossils can be interpreted as evidence of preexisting life.
- Recognize and explain methods by which scientists determine the sequence of geological events, and the life forms and environmental conditions that existed in past geologic eras.
- Describe the geologic time scale and provide examples of major geological and biological events of each era.
- Recognize the major historic contributions to interpreting sedimentary rock layers made by James Hutton and Charles Lyell.

PREPARE

Approximate lesson time is 60 minutes.

ASSESS

Unit Assessment: Geologic History Unit Assessment, Part 1 (*Online*)

You will complete an online assessment of the main objectives covered so far in this unit. Follow the instructions online. Your assessment will be scored by the computer.

Unit Assessment: Geologic History Unit Assessment, Part 2 (*Offline*)

Complete an offline Unit Assessment. Your learning coach will score this part of the Assessment.

Student Guide
Lesson 1. Optional: Your Choice

Explore earth's interior by peeling back each layer to discover what lies beneath. Find out what the layers are made of, how they move and alter our landscape, and how scientists have used seismographs like the one pictured here to uncover the mysteries of the planet's depths.

Lesson Objectives
- Practice skills and reinforce concepts taught in this course.

PREPARE

Approximate lesson time is 60 minutes.

Student Guide
Lesson 2: The Center of the Earth

Let's go exploring—down to the center of the earth. Starting at the surface, you'll travel deep into different layers. Gather interesting facts along your journey. How far is it to the center? How hot is it there? (Hint: Really hot!)

Lesson Objectives

- Interpret a diagram that depicts the structure of the earth's interior.
- Compare temperature, pressure, and composition of earth's inner and outer cores.

PREPARE

Approximate lesson time is 60 minutes.

Advance Preparation

- You will need an unpeeled, hard-boiled egg for this lesson.

Materials

> For the Student
>
> > 🖥 Earth as an Egg
> >
> > eggs, hard-boiled
> >
> > knife, plastic
> >
> > napkin
> >
> > plate

Keywords and Pronunciation

asthenosphere (as-THE-nuh-sfir) : the upper part of the earth's mantle

cross section : a section formed by a plane cutting through an object

crust : the outermost, solid layer of any planet or moon

exterior : the outer surface or part

interior : the inside of anything

lithosphere (LIH-the-sfir) : the rocky outer layer of the solid earth, averaging about 100 km in depth; the lithosphere includes the continents, islands, and the entire ocean floor

mantle : the part of earth that is beneath the crust and is made up of rock; about 84 percent of the earth's volume is in the mantle

molten : made liquid by heat, melted

plasticity (pla-STIS-i-tee) : capable of being molded

LEARN
Activity 1: A Look at the Earth's Layers *(Online)*

Activity 2: Earth as an Egg *(Offline)*
Demonstrations are a good way to understand new information. In this activity, you will demonstrate the layers of the earth using an egg as a model.

Safety
Use the knife with caution and with adult supervision.

Activity 3: The Center of the Earth *(Offline)*
Lesson Review
Review what you have learned about earth's interior. When finished, place your completed lesson review sheet in your Science Notebook.
Directions
Though no one has ever reached the layers below the crust, technology has helped scientists figure out what may lie deep within. If you were able to make the trip to the center of the earth, would you know what layer you've reached?

Where are you if…

1. You have reached an area where waves from earthquakes do not travel?_____

2. You are drilling through the thinnest part of earth's crust? _____

3. You are in the hottest part of the earth's interior? _____

4. You are surrounded by molten, flowing rock? _____

5. You are located in the area of least pressure? _____

6. You are located between the crust and the asthenosphere? _____

7. Rocks around you show plasticity? _____

ASSESS

Lesson Assessment: The Center of the Earth *(Online)*
You will complete an online assessment covering the main objectives of this lesson. Your assessment will be scored by the computer.

Name _____   Date _____

Earth as an Egg

Using an egg as a model, you can learn about the structure of the earth's interior.

Materials:

egg, hard-boiled
plate
napkin
plastic knife

Procedure:

1. Study the exterior of the egg.

2. Tap the egg lightly on all sides until the shell shows a few cracks.

3. Press lightly on the egg to move the cracked shell. Try to make a few pieces of shell collide into one another.

4. Press a piece of the cracked shell into the second layer of the egg, forcing pieces of egg to the top.

5. Cut the egg in half. Study the cross-section.

Observations:

1. What part of the earth did the eggshell represent?

    _____

2. What layer of "earth" showed through when you cracked the shell?

    _____

3. What layer of "earth" did the yolk represent?

    _____

4. Think about it: Which action could have demonstrated an earthquake?

    _____

5. Think about it: Which action demonstrated an eruption of lava as through a volcano?

    _____

Study the diagram below. Label each layer of the earth.

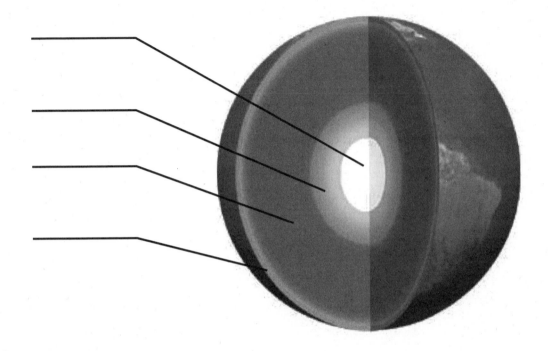

Student Guide
Lesson 3: Continental Drift

Look closely at a map of the earth and you will see that the shapes of certain continents look like they could fit together like a jigsaw puzzle. Early explorers, mapmakers, and scientists noticed it, too. Explore the evidence related to this earth-shattering observation.

Lesson Objectives

- Summarize continental drift as an example of a scientific theory that changed in response to new evidence.
- Define and explain Pangaea.

PREPARE

Approximate lesson time is 60 minutes.

Materials

For the Student

  🖳 Continents Map

  🖳 Investigating a Supercontinent

 highlighter

 construction paper

 glue or tape

 scissors

Keywords and Pronunciation

Theory of Continental Drift : the theory that the continents were previously joined together, and over time broke up and slowly drifted apart to their present positions

Abraham Ortelius (AY-bruh-ham or-TEL-ee-uhs)

Alfred Wegener (AHL-frayt VAY-guh-nuhr)

continental drift : the slow movement of continental plates over earth´s surface

Gondwanaland (gawn-DWAH-nuh-land)

Laurasia (law-RAY-zhuh)

mesosaurus (meh-soh-SAWR-uhs)

Pangaea (pan-JEE-uh) : the name scientists give to a supercontinent that once existed on earth

LEARN
Activity 1: A New Theory *(Online)*

Activity 2: Investigating a Supercontinent *(Offline)*

Scientists often must work together to develop their ideas. Though Alfred Wegener was the first to put together many details supporting the theory of continental drift, much of the information came from the contributions of other scientists.

Examine the evidence gathered by many scientists that supports the hypothesis of a once-existing supercontinent called Pangaea.

Activity 3: Continental Drift *(Offline)*

Lesson Review

Review what you have learned about earth's supercontinents. When finished, place your completed lesson review sheet in your Science Notebook.

Word Bank

Fill in each blank a term or name from the Word Bank. You will use each term only once.

Abraham Ortelius	Alfred Wegener	continental drift	continents	fossils
Gondwanaland	Laurasia	mesosaurs	Pangaea	
plate tectonics				

The idea that (1)_____ on the earth's surface change their position over long periods of time was first proposed in the 1500 by mapmakers including (2) _____. As explorers provided information about the shape of coastlines, mapmakers noticed that different landmasses, for example Africa and South America, seemed to fit together like pieces of a puzzle.

Four hundred years later, (3) _____ developed the first scientific theory to suggest that continents had changed positions over time. This was the theory of (4)_____.

Evidence used to develop this theory came from the similarity of (5)_____ recovered from continents that are now far apart. For example, freshwater reptiles known as (6)_____ lived in both Africa and South America.

Wegener's theory described a supercontinent, called (7)_____ that in her view as a scientist, existed about 200 million years ago. This large continent broke apart to form two landmasses.

(8)_____, in the northern hemisphere, broke apart further to form Europe, Asia, and North America. In the southern hemisphere, (9)_____, broke apart to form Africa, South America, Australia, Antarctica, and India.

Although this theory was not initially accepted, additional evidence convinced scientists that continents really do move.

ASSESS

Lesson Assessment: Continental Drift, Part 1 *(Online)*

You will complete an online assessment covering the main objectives of this lesson. Your assessment will be scored by the computer.

Lesson Assessment: Continental Drift, Part 2 *(Offline)*

You will complete an offline assessment covering the main objectives of this lesson. Your learning coach will score this assessment.

Name _____   Date _____

Investigating a Supercontinent

Shapes of Coastlines

1. Use your world map to study the edges of Africa and South America. Describe the match between them.

   _____

2. Cut the continents from the Continent Map. Try to arrange them on construction paper as one large landmass according to their shapes, but do not glue them yet. Notice the locations of any overlapping areas.

Mountain Ranges

Many mountain ranges that today appear on one continent are similar in age and form to mountain ranges on another continent. Some of these mountain ranges are shown on your continent cutouts. They are numbered according to those ranges that are similar to one another.

3. Check the landmass you created to see if the common mountain ranges line up with one another. Make any changes in your model now that you know about the mountain ranges.

Fossils

Several fossils are found on certain landmasses but not on others. Look at each landmass. Using the key, notice which fossils were found on each landmass.

4. Which fossils were found in both Africa and South America?

   _____

5. Adjust your model based on the fossil information.

Glacier Evidence

The map below shows where evidence of ice sheets 300 million years old has been found in the Southern Hemisphere. The dashed line on the map connects all the places where plowed rock and sediment have been found on the continents. The arrows show the direction of glacier movement.

Name _____   Date _____

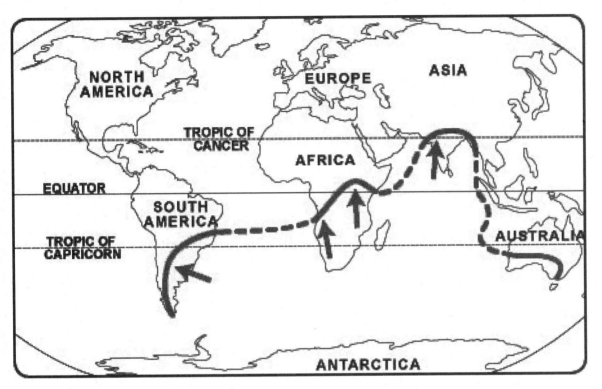

6. Use a highlighter to draw the information about glaciers onto the landmasses you have been arranging on the construction paper.

7. Make any changes in your model now that you know about glacial evidence.

When you are satisfied with the model you've created, glue your landmasses to the construction paper, and then answer the questions below.

Questions

8. What kinds of evidence can be used to show that a supercontinent once existed?

    _____

    _____

9. In your own words, explain the theory of continental drift.

    _____

    _____

10. Why do you think it took so long for scientists to accept the idea of continental drift?

    _____

    _____

11. What other evidence would you like to have to prove that the earth's surface has moved and is moving? What other questions would you like answered and explained?

    _____

Name   Date

Continents Map

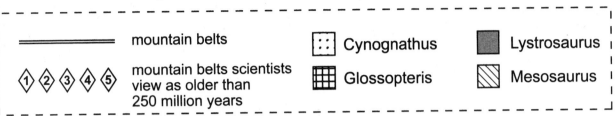

- ═══ mountain belts
- ◇1◇2◇3◇4◇5 mountain belts scientists view as older than 250 million years
- ⬚ Cynognathus
- ⊞ Glossopteris
- ■ Lystrosaurus
- ▨ Mesosaurus

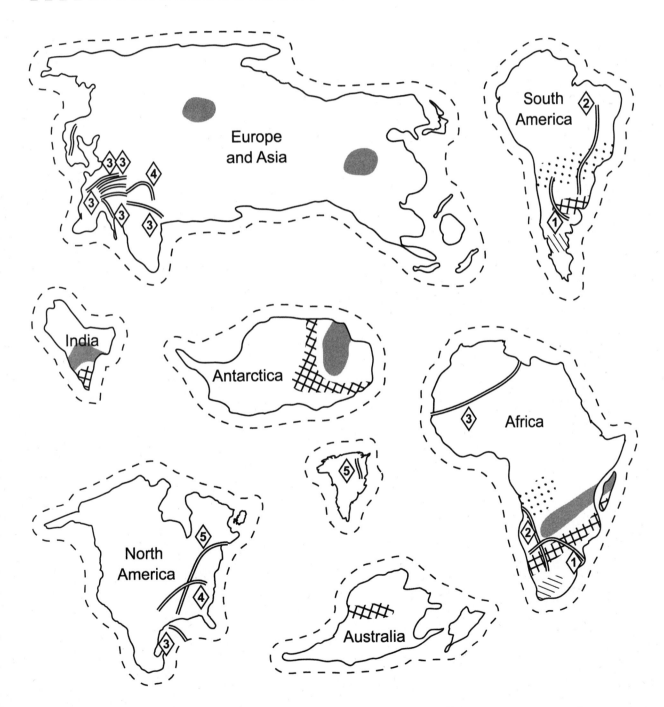

Name _____ Date _____

Continental Drift, Part 2 Lesson Assessment

Read each question carefully, and then write the answer on the lines provided.

1. Explain how mountain chains provide evidence to support the theory of continental drift.

    _____

    _____

2. What is one reason why many geologists did not at first accept the theory of continental drift?

    _____

    _____

Student Guide
Lesson 4: Seafloor Geography

During the last 50 years of detailed seafloor mapping, scientists have discovered important information about the ocean floor.

Studies revealed that the ocean floor is not featureless and is dynamic. It provides evidence explaining how continents can move throughout long periods of time.

Try an early method of seafloor mapping using weighted lines.

Lesson Objectives

- Identify features of the ocean floor.
- Explain how ocean floor mapping led to information that advanced the theory of continental drift.

PREPARE

Approximate lesson time is 60 minutes.

Advance Preparation

- This lesson presents information consistent with the general scientific consensus about the age of the earth.

Materials

For the Student

- Activity Instructions
- Graph Paper

books (3)

meter stick

tissue box

chairs (2)

markers or crayons

ruler

scissors

string - about 3 meters

trash can - small

washer, metal

Keywords and Pronunciation

abyssal plain : a flat expanse of ocean floor

bathymetric (ba-thih-MEH-trihk) : a type of data collected from measurement of the depths of oceans, seas, or other large bodies of water

continental rise : a region of gentle slope between the continental slope and the main ocean floor

continental shelf : a shelf of undersea land reaching a depth of about 200 meters (656 feet), extending out from the shoreline

continental slope : the relatively steeply sloping undersea land extending from the outer edge of the continental shelf

guyot (GEE-oh) : a seamount with a flattened top

midocean ridge : a long, raised area in the ocean, with a depression or valley running along its top

seamount : a volcanic mountain that rises from the ocean floor and has its peak underwater

submarine canyon : a deep channel on the ocean floor, in the outer continental shelf, in the continental slope, or in the continental rise

---

LEARN
Activity 1: Under the Sea *(Online)*

Activity 2: Mapping the Ocean Floor *(Offline)*
Mapping the Ocean Floor

Before ocean researchers used sound waves, early maps of the seafloor were made using weighted lines. These lines were dropped to the bottom of the seafloor, and then their length was measured. This activity will give you a good idea of how weighted lines were used to map the ocean floor.

Materials:

chairs, 2

scissors

ruler

meter stick

marker

string, about 3 meters

books, 3

trash can, small

tissue box

metal washer

notebook paper

Creating the Depth Scale:

1. Turn two chairs so the backs are facing each other, about 1 meter apart.
2. Tie a piece of string from one chair to the other so that there is exactly 1 meter of string between the chairs.
3. Use the marker and ruler to mark the string in 10-cm intervals.
4. Place the stack of books, the upside-down trash can, and the tissue box in a line underneath the string.
5. Cut another piece of string 30 cm taller than the height of the chairs.
6. Tie one end of the string to a metal washer.
7. To create a depth scale, use the marker and ruler to mark the string in 3-cm intervals.

Collecting Data

8. On a piece of notebook paper, make two columns and label them "Distance from Shore" and "Depth."

9. Move to the first mark on the string you stretched between the two chairs. Write "10 cm" in the "Distance from Shore" column.

10. Lower the depth scale string until the washer touches the floor or one of the objects.

11. Count the marks on the depth scale string and multiply by 3 to measure the depth at the first point. If the depth does not fall exactly on a marking, round off the measurement to the nearest mark.

12. Write the measurement in the "Depth" column.

13. Continue measuring at every 10-cm interval and record the measurements on your chart.

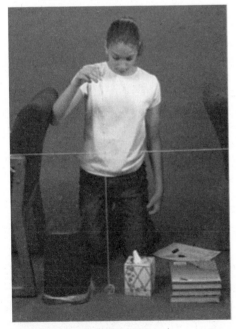

Creating the Seafloor Map

14. After all the measurements are taken, use the data from your chart to create a line graph on the graph paper. Your graph will illustrate what the "ocean floor" looks like.

13. Use a different colored marker to mark the string tied between the chairs in 5-cm intervals.

14. Repeat steps 8–12.

Questions

1. Compare the two line graphs. Which more closely matches the appearance of the ocean floor? Why?

_____

_____

2. Why is sonar a more accurate way of mapping the ocean floor than weighted lines?

_____

_____

ASSESS

Lesson Assessment: Seafloor Geography (*Online*)

You will complete an offline assessment covering the main objectives of this lesson. Your learning coach will score this assessment.

Name _____ Date _____

Seafloor Geography Activity Instructions
Activity 2. Mapping the Ocean Floor *(Offline)*

Mapping the Ocean Floor

Before ocean researchers used sound waves, early maps of the seafloor were made using weighted lines. These lines were dropped to the bottom of the seafloor, and then their length was measured. This activity will give you a good idea of how weighted lines were used to map the ocean floor.

Materials:

chairs, 2
scissors
ruler
meter stick
marker
string, about 3 meters
books, 3
trash can, small
tissue box
metal washer
notebook paper

Creating the Depth Scale:

1. Turn two chairs so the backs are facing each other, about 1 meter apart.

2. Tie a piece of string from one chair to the other so that there is exactly 1 meter of string between the chairs.

3. Use the marker and ruler to mark the string in 10-cm intervals.

4. Place the stack of books, the upsidedown trash can, and the tissue box in a line underneath the string.

5. Cut another piece of string 30 cm taller than the height of the chairs.

6. Tie one end of the string to a metal washer.

7. To create a depth scale, use the marker and ruler to mark the string in 3-cm intervals.

Collecting Data

8. On a piece of notebook paper, make two columns and label them "Distance from Shore" and "Depth."

9. Move to the first mark on the string you stretched between the two chairs. Write "10 cm" in the "Distance from Shore" column.

10. Lower the depth scale string until the washer touches the floor or one of the objects.

11. Count the marks on the depth scale string and multiply by 3 to measure the depth at the first point. If the depth does not fall exactly on a marking, round off the measurement to the nearest mark.

12. Write the measurement in the "Depth" column.

13. Continue measuring at every 10-cm interval and record the measurements on your chart.

Creating the Seafloor Map

14. After all the measurements are taken, use the data from your chart to create a line graph on the graph paper. Your graph will illustrate what the "ocean floor" looks like.

13. Use a different colored marker to mark the string tied between the chairs in 5-cm intervals.

14. Repeat steps 8–12.

Questions

1. Compare the two line graphs. Which more closely matches the appearance of the ocean floor? Why?

   _____

   _____

2. Why is sonar a more accurate way of mapping the ocean floor than weighted lines?

   _____

   _____

Name _____   Date _____

Seafloor Geography Graph Paper

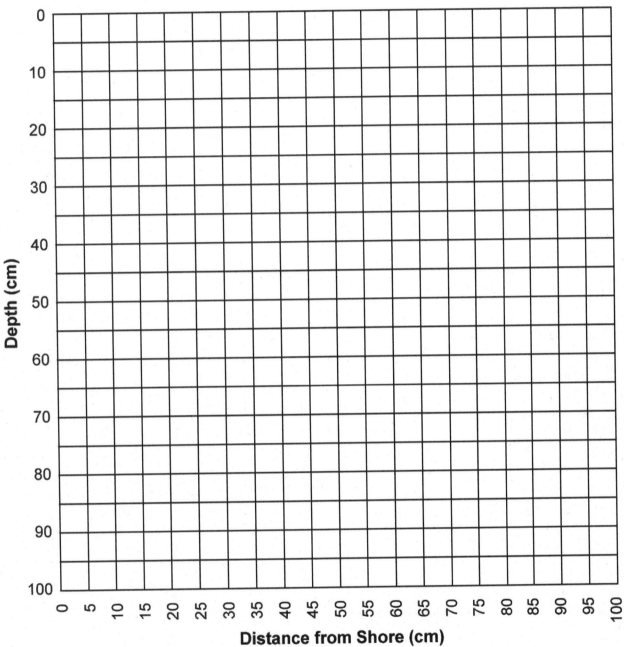

Name _____ Date _____

Seafloor Geography Lesson Assessment

1. Fill in each blank with a term from the Word Bank. You will use each term only once, and you will use all of the terms.

Word Bank

continental shelf	guyot	deep-sea trench
		seamount
continental rise	abyssal plain	continental slope

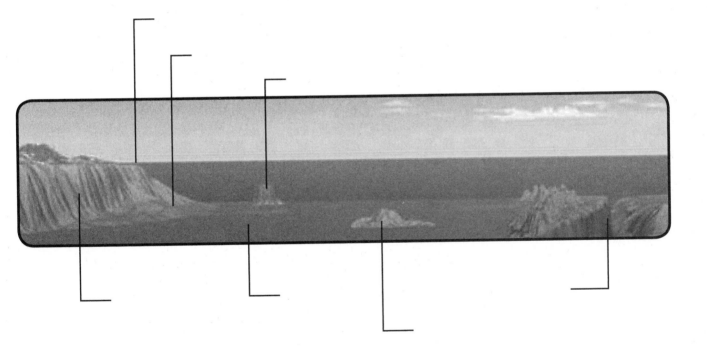

2. Mapping the seafloor resulted in two pieces of information that made the theory of continental drift sound more likely. What were they?

_____

_____

_____

_____

Student Guide
Lesson 5: Seafloor Spreading

The early 1960s brought new evidence to support the theory of continental drift. This evidence, including magnetic patterns found in rocks on the ocean floor, led many scientists to reconsider the theory, which suggested that parts of the earth's crust had actually moved—and continue to move today.

Lesson Objectives

- Explain how magnetism in rocks was used as evidence to support the concept of seafloor spreading.
- Describe how seafloor spreading results in the formation of new crust.

PREPARE

Approximate lesson time is 60 minutes.

Materials

For the Student

🖥 What's the Spread?

calculator

ruler

Keywords and Pronunciation

paleomagnetism (pay-lee-oh-MAG-nuh-tih-zuhm) : magnetic qualities "frozen" into rocks when they are formed, including the direction of the magnetic field

LEARN
Activity 1: Magnetism and the Seafloor *(Online)*

Activity 2: What's the Spread? *(Offline)*
Complete the activity to find out when the Mid-Atlantic Ridge started its spread and how far continents have drifted since you were born.

ASSESS

Lesson Assessment: Seafloor Spreading, Part 1 (*Online*)
You will complete an online assessment covering the main objectives of this lesson. Your assessment will be scored by the computer.

Lesson Assessment: Seafloor Spreading, Part 2 (*Offline*)
You will complete an offline assessment covering the main objectives of this lesson. Your learning coach will score this assessment.

Name   Date

What's the Spread?

Each year, new seafloor is added at the Mid-Atlantic Ridge. The Atlantic Ocean widens causing North and South America to move farther away from Europe and Africa. Close to the ridge, rocks are younger. As you move away from the ridge, the rocks become older.

    1. Where would you find the oldest sections of seafloor, near the continents or near the Mid-Atlantic Ridge?

The rate of seafloor spreading has not been the same over time. In this activity, you will calculate the average rate of seafloor spreading, and then determine when the seafloor started to spread.

Materials

Ruler
Calculator
Geologic Time line in Unit Resources

Procedure

Working with Map Scales

Below is a map of a section of the North Atlantic. You can see the coastlines of North America and Africa. On both sides of the Mid-Atlantic Ridge strips of seafloor are labeled with their ages in millions of years. Note the map scale.

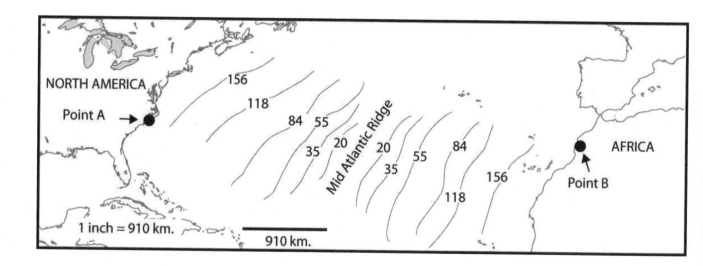

1. What is the scale of the map? For this activity, you will use inches.

   _____in =_____ km

2. Choose one strip of seafloor rock. Write the age of the rock here:_____million years

3. Use your ruler to measure the distance of the strip from the Mid-Atlantic Ridge. _____ inches

4. Using the calculator, divide the answer to #3 by 910 to figure out its distance in kilometers.
   _____ km.

Determining Rate of Spreading

Use the age of the rock you have chosen and its distance from the Mid-Atlantic Ridge to calculate seafloor spreading.

5. First you will find out how fast the seafloor is moving away from the ridge on one side. Use the calculator to divide the answer to #4 by the answer to #2.

   #4 _____ km ÷ #2 _____ million years = km/1million years

6. Now find out how fast the seafloor widens every 1 million years. Multiply the answer you got in #5 by 2. The seafloor spreads at a rate of _____ km every 1 million years.

When Did the Seafloor Start Spreading?

The distance between Point A and Point B, or the coasts of Africa and North America, is 4,550 km. Using your answer to #6, find out when the Atlantic Ocean began to open. Divide your answer in # 6 by 4,550 km to find out.

7. #6 _____ ÷ 4,550 =_____ million years ago.

8. Look at the Geologic Timeline. During what geologic period did the Atlantic start to open?

   _____

Challenge

See if you can figure out how much the distance between North America and Africa has increased since you were born.

9. #6 _____ x 0.62 x 5,280 x 12 x 0.000001 = _____ inches/year

10. How far, in inches, has the distance between North America and Africa increased since you were born?
    _____ inches

11. How much does the distance increase during the average lifetime of 82 years?
    _____ inches

Super Challenge

12. How much closer were the continents when Columbus crossed the Atlantic in 1492?
    _____ inches

Name _____   Date _____

Seafloor Spreading, Part 2 Lesson Assessment

Read and answer the questions below.

10 pts.

1. Explain how seafloor spreading results in new oceanic crust. You may include a drawing in your explanation.

_____

_____

_____

10 pts.

2. Explain how a prediction and then evidence of magnetism in rocks on the ocean floor proved that the seafloor spreads.

_____

_____

_____

_____

Student Guide
Lesson 6: Plate Tectonics

Scientists concluded that earth is composed of many different-sized plates. This information led to a new theory that explained movement of continents and geologic activity such as earthquakes and volcanoes. Understand how dramatic, volcanic events, such as the eruption of this underwater volcano near Japan, align great plates on which continents move.

Lesson Objectives

- Summarize the theory of plate tectonics.
- Summarize major scientific evidence for continental drift.

PREPARE

Approximate lesson time is 60 minutes.

Materials

For the Student

🖵 Earth's Lithospheric Plates

pencils, colored 12

Keywords and Pronunciation

convection (kuhn-VEK-shuhn) : the transfer of heat by the circulation or movement of the heated parts of a liquid or gas

convergent plate boundary : a boundary at which tectonic plates are moving toward one another or colliding

divergent plate boundary : a plate boundary where two plates move away from each other

seismograph (SIYZ-muh-graf) : an instrument used to record earthquake waves

Theory of Plate Tectonics : the scientific theory that earth's crust is made up of about 20 huge plates that are always moving very slowly. According to the Theory of Plate Tectonics, all seven continents were once part of a super continent called Pangaea.

transform plate boundaries : a plate boundary where two plates move in opposite directions alongside one another

LEARN
Activity 1: Earth's Plates (Online)

Activity 2: Forming a Theory (Offline)

Answer the questions using the World Geology map on screen 5 of this lesson. You may also use the U.S. Geological Survey's Plates of the Earth map as a reference.

http://earthquake.usgs.gov/learn/topics/plate_tectonics/plates.php

Forming a Theory

1. Wegener formed the theory of continental drift in 1912. What prevented research of the ocean floor, paleomagnetism, and earthquakes at that time?

_____

_____

_____

_____

2. If many different observations can all be explained by the same theory, does that make the theory true? Does it make the theory more likely?

_____

_____

_____

3. What evidence is there to suggest that the earth is composed of tectonic plates?

_____

_____

_____

_____

Forming a Theory

4. What evidence is there to suggest that tectonic plates move?

_____

_____

_____

5. Click Topography and Major Plates on the World Geology map. Describe the topography at the boundaries between the following pairs of plates: South American and Nazca, Indian and Eurasian, and Pacific and North American.

_____

_____

_____

6. Observe the border between the Indian plate and the Somali plate. Do you see the same landforms as at the boundary between the Indian plate and the Eurasian plate? Explain.

_____

_____

_____

7. Click Earthquakes and Major Plates on the World Geology map, and observe earthquake activity around the South American plate. Based on your observations, what can you conclude about lithospheric motion of the South American plate with the Nazca plate and the African plate? Explain your answer.

_____

_____

_____

_____

8. How certain do you feel that plate tectonic theory is correct? What evidence would you use to support your opinion?

_____

_____

_____

_____

ASSESS

Lesson Assessment: Plate Tectonics (*Offline*)

You will complete an offline assessment covering the main objectives of this lesson. Your learning coach will score this assessment.

Name _____ Date _____

Earth's Lithospheric Plates

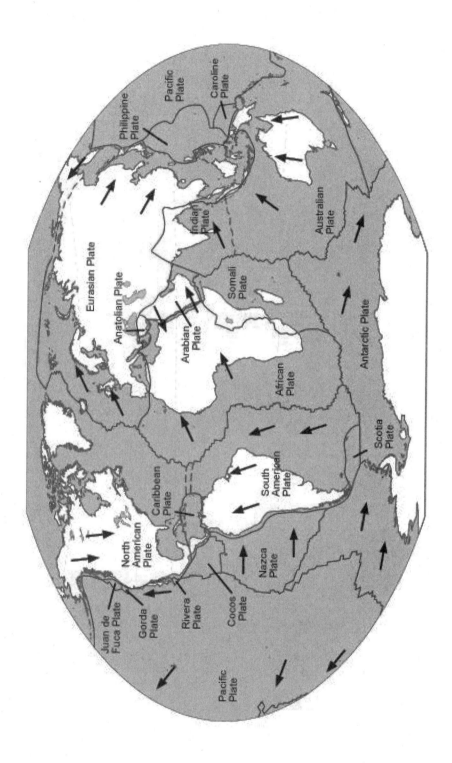

Name _____ Date _____

Plate Tectonics Lesson Assessment

Read and answer each question below.

1. After Wegener proposed the theory of continental drift, evidence was found to support it that led to the theory of plate tectonics. List four pieces of that evidence.

   a. _____

   b. _____

   c. _____

   d. _____

2. In your own words, describe the theory of plate tectonics and the action that occurs at plate boundaries. You may draw a picture to explain your answer.

   _____

   _____

   _____

   _____

Student Guide
Lesson 7: Energy of Convection

You have learned that plates on the earth's surface move. But how? Earth's plates are very large and very massive. Scientists think that two forces are responsible for plate movement: convection and gravity. In this lesson, you'll investigate how each of these forces are involved in plate movement.

Lesson Objectives

- Recognize that heat from the earth's interior reaches the surface through convection.
- Summarize the role of convection and gravity in the movement of plates.

PREPARE

Approximate lesson time is 60 minutes.

Materials

> For the Student
>
> > 💻 Sources of Plate Motion
> >
> > pencil, colored - 1 red, 1 green.
> >
> > 💻 Lesson Review

Keywords and Pronunciation

asthenosphere (as-THE-nuh-sfir) : the upper part of the earth´s mantle

convection (kuhn-VEK-shuhn) : the transfer of heat by the circulation or movement of the heated parts of a liquid or gas

convergent plates : plates that are moving toward one another

divergent plate boundary : a plate boundary where two plates move away from each other

gravity : a universal force that every mass exerts on every other mass

mantle : the part of earth that is beneath the crust and is made up of rock; about 84 percent of the earth´s volume is in the mantle

ridge push : at a divergent boundary, the pushing force on a tectonic plate caused by gravity acting on its elevated edge

slab pull : at a convergent boundary, the pulling force on a tectonic plate that causes its edge to sink into the mantle

subduction (suhb-DUHK-shuhn)

LEARN
Activity 1: Energy of Convection *(Online)*

Activity 2: Sources of Plate Motion (Offline)

Purpose

Explore the process of plate movement.

Materials

red color pencil

green color pencil

Introduction

Recall that scientists think gravity acting on the edges of tectonic plates is a factor in their movement. These effects are called "ridge push" and "slab pull." You can model these effects with a chair and a bed.

Ridge push

If you sit on a chair and let gravity pull you down into a slouching position, you'll notice your legs go out. Your upper body falling down pushes your legs out and away, like the ridge of a tectonic plate falling down pushes on the other end of the plate. The other end of the plate moves out and away from the pushing part of the plate.

Slab pull

Lie on a bed, facing down, with your upper body hanging just a little over the edge. Slowly and carefully let your upper body fall toward the floor. Notice that your legs move toward the edge of the bed. How is this like slab pull? Your upper body falling down pulls your legs toward the edge of the bed like the sinking slab of a tectonic plate would pull the rest of the plate toward it.

Sources of Plate Motion

The motion of earth's tectonic plates is due in part to convection, as well as to ridge push and slab pull. Convection is a motion in a fluid or plastic material caused by heating material below and cooling material above.

Questions

Study the first illustration on the Sources of Plate Motion sheet. Notice how convection currents in the mantle can affect plates in the lithosphere above. Do you see a connection between the directions of convection currents and the motion of the plates? To see the connection more clearly, trace the motion of the currents in red. Then trace the motion of the plates in green.

Use the online lesson to help you answer the questions below.

1. What processes drive motion of the plates?

_____

_____

2. What temperature and density changes occur in convection cells of a fluid or plastic material?

_____

_____

3. How can the mantle flow by convection if it is a solid?

_____

_____

4. Describe what occurs at mid-ocean ridges.

_____

Study the second illustration on the Sources of Plate Motion activity sheet. This map shows the motion of the earth's plates.

Answer the questions below.

5. Find the Nazca Plate and the South American Plate. How are they different? Are they moving toward or away from each other? Use the map on Screen 2 and refer to the arrows on the map on the Sources of Plate Motion sheet to help you.

_____

_____

6. List the kinds of features you might expect to see near the edges of plates, like these two plates that are coming together.

_____

_____

7. How is the Nazca Plate moving in relation to the Pacific Plate?

_____

_____

8. What kinds of features would you expect to see at the edges of two plates, like these that are moving apart at their boundary?

_____

_____

Think and Reflect

9. How are convection currents in the mantle (geosphere) and in the oceans (hydrosphere) similar? How are they different?

_____

_____

Activity 3: Energy of Convection *(Offline)*

ASSESS

Lesson Assessment: Energy of Convection, Part 1 *(Online)*

You will complete an online assessment covering the main objectives of this lesson. Your assessment will be scored by the computer.

Lesson Assessment: Energy of Convection, Part 2 *(Offline)*

You will complete an offline assessment covering the main objectives of this lesson. Your learning coach will score this assessment.

Name _____   Date _____

Sources of Plate Motion

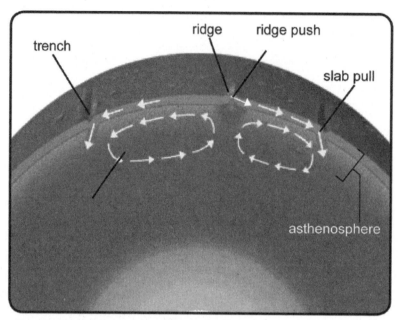

Convection Currents and Plate Motion

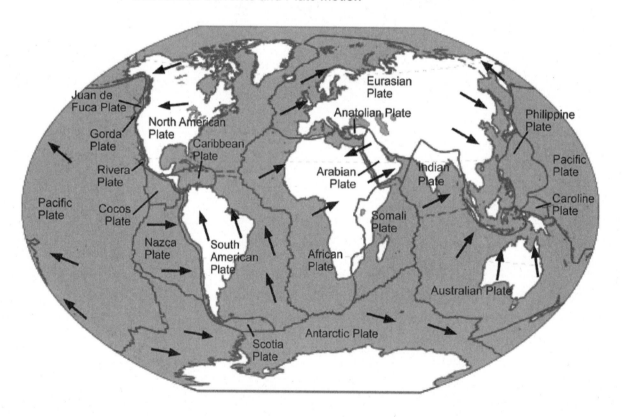

Name   Date

Energy of Convection Lesson Review

Fill in each blank with a term or name from the Word Bank. Use each term only once, but use all of the terms.

Word Bank

asthenosphere   convection

ridge   ridge push

slab pull   trench

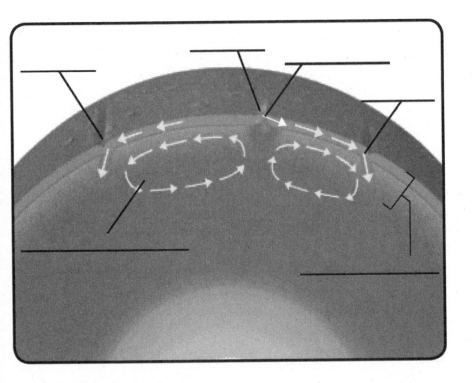

Name _____   Date _____

Energy of Convection Lesson Assessment

1. Explain how gravity effects the movement of plates at mid-ocean ridges.

    _____

    _____

2. How does convection in the asthenosphere contribute to the movement of tectonic plates?

    _____

    _____

    _____

Student Guide
Lesson 8: Plate Boundaries

Tectonic plates are not all moving in the same direction or at the same speed. Some are moving in the same direction, but at different speeds. Some are moving toward each other, and some are moving apart. What happens at the boundaries where two plates meet? Let's find out more in this lesson.

Lesson Objectives
- Compare the properties of continental and oceanic crust.
- Describe the types of motion that occur at the boundaries of earth's plates.
- Interpret a map of plate boundaries on the earth.

PREPARE

Approximate lesson time is 60 minutes.

Materials
For the Student
- 📖 Lithospheric Plates
- 📖 Lesson Review

Keywords and Pronunciation

Aleutian (uh-LOO-shuhn)

asthenosphere (as-THE-nuh-sfir) : the upper part of the earth's mantle

convection (kuhn-VEK-shuhn) : the transfer of heat by the circulation or movement of the heated parts of a liquid or gas

convergent plates : plates that are moving toward one another

divergent plate boundary : a plate boundary where two plates move away from each other

Himalaya (hih-muh-LAY-uh)

hot spot : a hot place in the mantle where magma rises, often melting the crust above to form a volcano

lithosphere (LIH-the-sfir) : the rocky outer layer of the solid earth, averaging about 100 km in depth; the lithosphere includes the continents, islands, and the entire ocean floor

magnesium (mag-NEE-zee-uhm)

Mariana Islands (mar-ee-A-nuh)

San Andreas (san an-DRAY-uhs)

subduction (suhb-DUHK-shuhn)

transform plate boundaries : a plate boundary where two plates move in opposite directions alongside one another

LEARN
Activity 1: Plate Boundaries (Online)

Activity 2: Slow Motion: Divergent and Transform Boundaries (Offline)

Print a new copy of the map of Earth's Lithospheric Plates to answer the questions. You may use the activity Explore: Plate Boundaries if necessary.

1. Study the map of earth's lithospheric plates. Identify and describe the crust for one plate with mostly oceanic crust and for one plate with a large amount of continental crust.

_____

_____

_____

_____

2. Study the motion of the plates as shown by the arrows. Use red to color the touching borders of plates that are moving away from one another. Are these divergent or transform boundaries?

_____

_____

_____

_____

3. Use green to color the touching borders of plates that are moving in opposite directions alongside one another. Are these divergent or transform boundaries?

_____

_____

_____

_____

4. What kinds of plate motion are associated with mid-ocean ridges and undersea volcanic mountains?

_____

_____

_____

_____

Activity 3: Plate Boundaries (Offline)

ASSESS

Lesson Assessment: Plate Boundaries, Part 1 (Online)
You will complete an online assessment covering the main objectives of this lesson. Your assessment will be scored by the computer.

Lesson Assessment: Plate Boundaries, Part 2 (Offline)
You will complete an offline assessment covering the main objectives of this lesson. Your learning coach will score this assessment.

Name _____ Date _____

Earth's Lithospheric Plates

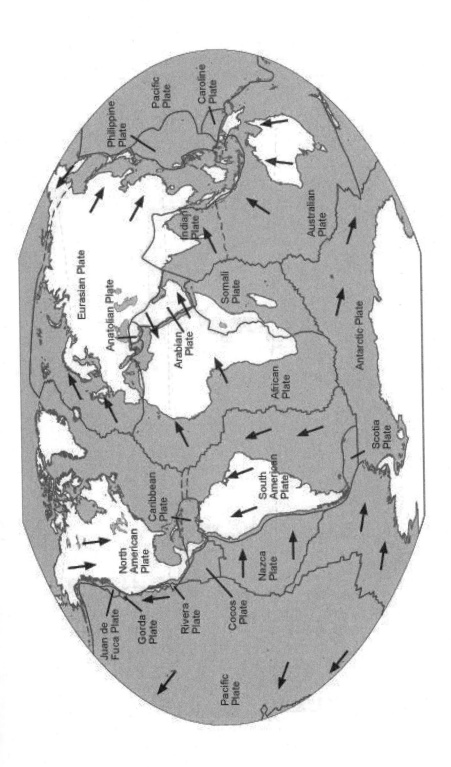

Name _____   Date _____

Plate Boundaries Lesson Review

Review what you have learned about earth's spheres. When finished, place your completed lesson review sheet in your Science Notebook.

Review what you have learned about plate boundaries. Use the map above to fill in the table below. The first one has been completed for you.

Boundary	Type of Boundary	Types of Lithosphere at the Boundary	Description
1. North American – African	divergent	both are oceanic	The North American and African plates are moving apart.
2. Pacific-Philippine			
3. Indian-Eurasian			
4. Australian-Antarctic			
5. Somali-African			
6. Pacific-North American			
7. Nazca-South American			

Name _____   Date _____

Plate Boundaries, Part 2 Lesson Assessment

1. Explain why convergent oceanic plates subduct, but continental plates do not usually respond in this way.

10 pts.

2. Complete the chart to compare different types of the plate boundaries. Add the words *transform, convergent,* and *divergent* to the chart.

Boundary Type	Description of Plate Motion
	plates slide past each other in opposite directions
	plates move away from each other
	plates move toward each other

Student Guide
Lesson 9: Landforms

There are many beautiful mountain ranges around the world — the Andes in South America, the Himalayas in Asia, and the Rocky Mountains in North America. These mountains did not always exist. They formed when tectonic plates collided with one another. Tectonic plates are in constant motion, sometimes moving toward one another and sometimes moving apart. At some places, the plates are moving in opposite directions, and they grind against one another. In this lesson, you will learn about what happens to the crust at the boundaries between these plates.

Lesson Objectives

- Explain the relationship between geologic activity and plate motion.
- Identify the landforms that result from different types of motion at plate boundaries.

PREPARE

Approximate lesson time is 60 minutes.

Materials

For the Student

- Earth's Lithospheric Plates
- Lesson Review

Keywords and Pronunciation

asthenosphere (as-THE-nuh-sfir) : the upper part of the earth's mantle

convergent plates : plates that are moving toward one another

divergent plate boundary : a plate boundary where two plates move away from each other

hot spot : a hot place in the mantle where magma rises, often melting the crust above to form a volcano

transform plate boundaries : a plate boundary where two plates move in opposite directions alongside one another

LEARN
Activity 1: Landforms *(Online)*

Activity 2: Slow Motion: Divergent and Transform Boundaries *(Offline)*

Part 1

Print a copy of the map of Earth's Lithospheric Plates to answer the questions. You may use the online activity to help you if necessary.

1. Study the motion of the plates as shown by the arrows. Use blue to color the boundaries of plates that are moving toward each other. What type of plate boundaries are these?

   _____

2. Name two plates that share a convergent boundary. Tell if the crust at the boundary is oceanic or continental, or both.

   _____

   _____

   _____

3. When two continental plates collide, what is the major resulting landform?

   _____

   _____

4. Describe three things that could happen as an oceanic plate moves below another oceanic plate or a continental plate.

   _____

   _____

   _____

   _____

5. How is plate motion at convergent boundaries different from motion at transform boundaries? From motion at divergent boundaries?_____

   _____

   _____

   _____

Part 2

In the Explore activity, we pointed out volcanic activity that occurs where plates converge. We mentioned the Aleutian Islands, the Mariana Islands, and the Tonga Islands as resulting from such activity. Find them on your K12 Wall Map and plot them on your Lithospheric Plates Map. Notice where they are in relation to convergent plate boundaries. Also find the Peru-Chile Trench and notice its relationship with the Nazca and South American plates.

Activity 3: Landforms (Offline)

ASSESS

Lesson Assessment: Landforms, Part 1 (Online)

You will complete an online assessment covering the main objectives of this lesson. Your assessment will be scored by the computer.

Lesson Assessment: Landforms, Part 2 (Offline)

You will complete an offline assessment covering the main objectives of this lesson. Your learning coach will score this assessment.

Name _____ Date _____

Earth's Lithospheric Plates

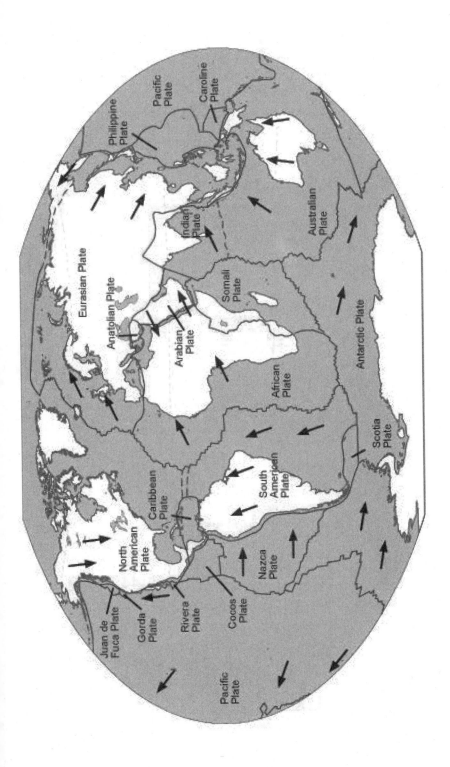

Name   Date

Landforms Lesson Review

Review what you have learned about earth's spheres. When finished, place your completed lesson review sheet in your Science Notebook.

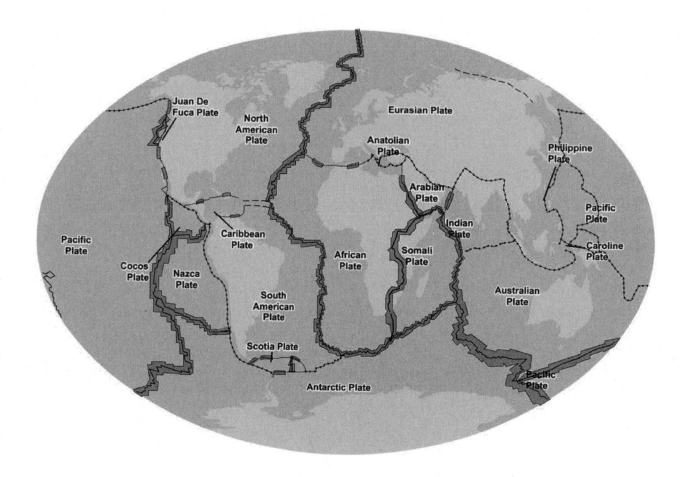

Review what you have learned about landforms. Use the map above to fill in the table below. You may also use the online World Map to help you. The first row has been completed for you.

Boundary	Type of Boundary	Volcanoes Likely?	Mountains Forming?	Trench Forming?
1. North American–African	divergent	no	no	no
2. Pacific-Philippine				
3. Indian-Eurasian				
4. Australian-Antarctic				
5. Somali-African				
6. Pacific-Australian				
7. Cocos-North American				

Name _____ Date _____

Landforms, Part 2 Lesson Assessment

1. Explain how convergent boundaries of oceanic crust form islands.

2. Identify the type of plate boundary and describe the plate motion that results in the formation of deep ocean trenches.

Student Guide
Lesson 10: LAB: Plate Boundaries and Structural Geography

You are probably not strong enough to pick up a large rock, and then bend or break it by pushing and pulling on it. These changes in rock take very strong forces and may take very long times. Scientists make models to study the effects of stress from forces within the earth. Make a model of folded rock, simulate the forces that cause faults, and then work "in the field" observing examples of faulting and folding on earth.

Lesson Objectives

- Identify the landforms that result from different types of motion at plate boundaries.
- Compare convergent, divergent, and transform plate boundaries.

PREPARE

Approximate lesson time is 60 minutes.

Advance Preparation

- If you don't already have it, you will need a 1 1/2 x 4 x 8 inch foam block for the Modeling Faults activity.

Materials

For the Student

- 🖳 Modeling Folds Activity Instructions

   clay, modeling

   rolling pin

   ruler

   scissors

- 🖳 Modeling Faults

   foam block

   knife (metal or plastic)

   markers or crayons

   pencils, colored 12

- 🖳 Geologic Map

Keywords and Pronunciation

compression : stress on a material from a force or forces pushing inward from one or both ends

deformation (dee-fawr-MAY-shuhn)

shear : stress on a material from forces acting in opposite directions alongside one another

tension : stress on a material from a force or forces pulling outward from one or both ends

LEARN
Activity 1: Forces of the Earth *(Online)*

Activity 2: Modeling Folds *(Offline)*
Introduction
Faulting can occur quickly when an earthquake accompanies breaking of rock, releasing stress that has built up in the crust. However, changes in rock such as folding take place over a very long time. Folding of rock cannot be observed in nature while it happens. Scientists use models to understand many of the changes in rock.

Materials
modeling clay - at least three colors
rolling pin
scissors
ruler, metric

Procedure
1. Shape a large lump of clay into a long, rectangular-shaped rounded hill, about 10 cm long and 6 cm wide and 6 cm high, as shown. This is your base block.
2. Put another lump of clay onto wax paper. Use a rolling pin to flatten it into a sheet aout 5 mm thick. Lay the sheet over your base block and trim the edges.

3. Repeat step 2 with clay of different colors until you have five or six layers. Shape each layer with your fingers so it keeps almost the same shape as your base block.
4. Slowly use your fingertips to push the outer edges of the layers toward each other until they fold. You now have a block of folded rock layers.

5. Use the ruler to slice through your folded block. Make two slices as shown: one straight down through the block and the ohter horizontally, through the middle of the folds.

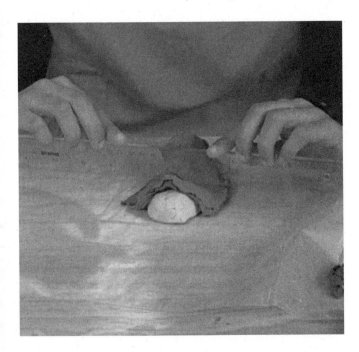

6. Observe the faces of the cuts you made. The vertical cut is what real folded rocks look like when exposed vertically by erosion or faulting, and the horizontal cut is what they look like when they are eroded away to a flat surface.

7. In the space to the below, sketch what the folds look like on each face of your block.

Activity 3: Modeling Faults *(Offline)*

There are three main types of faults. They are classified according to the direction of the movement of the two sides. This movement depends on the direction of the forces causing the movement. Print the Modeling Faults sheet, gather your materials, and begin the activity.

Safety

Activity 4: Geologic Structure and Maps - Part 1 *(Offline)*

Geologic maps have special symbols that tell where faults and folds exist. Many maps also have cross sections drawn, just as you saw when you modeled folds and faults. A cross section shows how the rocks are deformed and makes it easier to understand the forces involved. Use the Geologic Map to complete the following investigation.

Geologic Structure from Maps: Part 1 Geologic Map

1. Study the map and cross section. There are five rock layers shown, A through E. Color each layer a different color. Use the letters in the layers to help you.
2. Sediments are almost always deposited in flat layers. Does it appear that forces in the earth affected the rock layers in this region? What clues do you have?

_____

_____

3. Did pushing (compression), pulling (tension), or sideways forces (shear) in the rock layers produce the folds and faults?

_____

_____

_____

Geologic Structure from Maps: Part 2 Online photos

Now view photos online of faults around the world. See if you are able to tell which types of faults caused the rocks to form each structure.

You know how forces on rocks can cause rocks to bend or fold, or under some conditions, cause the rocks to fracture. Forces can also move rock up and down. You can use what you know to look at your community and describe what forces may have caused a certain landform to look a certain way. Use the online photos to answer the following questions:

Look at the photograph of faulted rock layers in British Columbia, Canada.

4. Do the rocks appear to have been pushed together, pulled apart, or to have slid past each other to make this formation? What type of fault is this?

_____

_____

Look at the photograph of a fault found in Klamath Falls, Oregon.

5. Was the rock pulled apart, pushed together, or did it slide past another rock to make this formation? What type of fault is this?

_____

_____

Activity 5: Geologic Structure and Maps - Part 2 *(Online)*

ASSESS

Lesson Assessment: LAB: Plate Boundaries and Structural Geography *(Online)*

Have an adult review your answers to the Modeling Folds lab, the Modeling Faults lab and the Geologic Structure and Maps activities and input the results online.

Lesson 10: LAB: Plate Boundaries and Structural Geography

Activity 2. Modeling Folds *(Offline)*

Introduction

Faulting can occur quickly when an earthquake accompanies breaking of rock, releasing stress that has built up in the crust. However, changes in rock such as folding take place over a very long time. Folding of rock cannot be observed in nature while it happens. Scientists use models to understand many of the changes in rock.

Materials

modeling clay - at least three colors
rolling pin
scissors
ruler, metric

Procedure

1. Shape a large lump of clay into a long, rectangular-shaped rounded hill, about 10 cm long and 6 cm wide and 6 cm high, as shown. This is your base block.

2. Put another lump of clay onto wax paper. Use a rolling pin to flatten it into a sheet about 5 mm thick. Lay the sheet over your base block and trim the edges.

3. Repeat step 2 with clay of different colors until you have five or six layers. Shape each layer with your fingers so it keeps almost the same shape as your base block.

4. Slowly use your fingertips to push the outer edges of the layers toward each other until they fold. You now have a block of folded rock layers.

5. Use the ruler to slice through your folded block. Make two slices as shown: one straight down through the block and the other horizontally, through the middle of the folds.

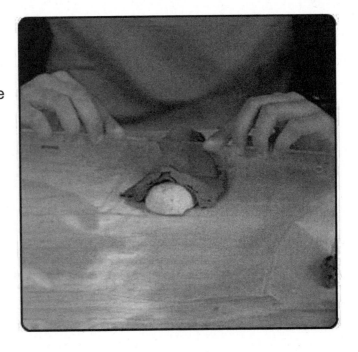

6. Observe the faces of the cuts you made. The vertical cut is what real folded rocks look like when exposed vertically by erosion or faulting, and the horizontal cut is what they look like when they are eroded away to a flat surface.

7. In the space to the right, sketch what the folds look like on each face of your block.

Name _____   Date _____

Geologic Map: Geologic Structure and Maps

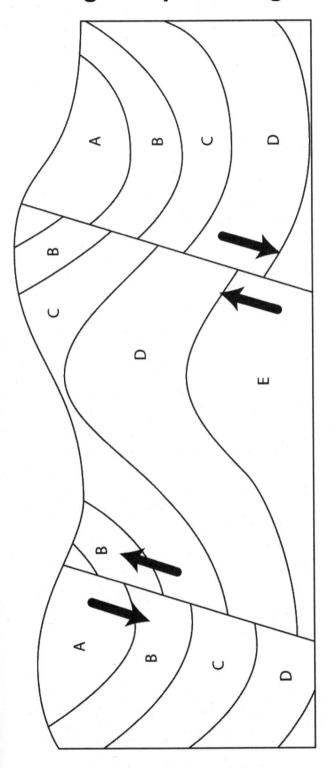

Name _____ Date _____

Modeling Faults

There are three main types of faults. They are classified according to the direction of the movement of the two sides. This movement depends on the direction of the forces causing the movement.

Fault Type	Direction of Forces	Result
Reverse	⇒ ⇐	Rocks are pushed together, one over the other.
Normal	⇐ ⇒	Rocks spread out, one pulling away from the other.
Strike-slip	⇐ ⇒	Rocks bend or break sideways, each sliding past the other.

Make the Model – Reverse Fault

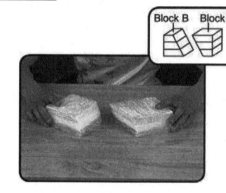

1. Use colored pencils or markers to create at least three horizontal layers on the sides of your blocks. Have an adult help you cut the block into two pieces at an angle, as shown.

2. Place the two cut blocks together, face-to-face. The left block is Block A. The right block is Block B. The side where the two cut surfaces touch is a fault line.

3. Slowly push the two pieces together so that Block A slides upward.

You have just modeled a reverse fault. Reverse faults are formed from pushing forces, also called *compression forces*. Study the picture of the reverse fault to the right. The first shows how your fault moved, looking from the side. Look closely at the direction of forces and the direction in which the blocks moved.

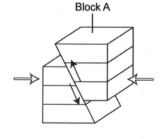

4. Which block has the foot wall?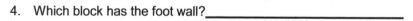

5. Which block has the hanging wall?_____

6. What type of plate boundary is typically associated with pushing or compression forces?

_____

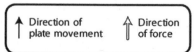

Make the Model - Normal Fault

7. Return the pieces to their original positions. Slowly pull Block B upward while keeping the joined faces in contact.

You just modeled a normal fault. Normal faults are formed from pulling forces, also called *tension forces*. Study the pictures below. Look closely at the directions of forces and the direction in which the plates moved.

8. What is the difference in the way the blocks moved, comparing the reverse fault with the normal fault?

_____

_____

9. Which block has the hanging wall?_____

10. Which block has the foot wall?_____

11. Of the three main types of plate boundaries (divergent, convergent, transform), which type is most likely to be associated with pulling or tension forces? _____

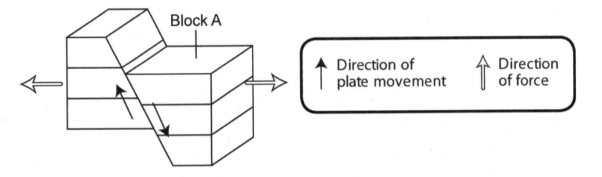

Block A

Direction of plate movement

Direction of force

Make the Model - Strike-Slip Fault

12. Return the blocks to their original positions. Move both blocks so they slide sideways past each other.

You just modeled a strike-slip fault. Strike-slip faults are formed from sideways forces, or *shear forces.* The blocks respond differently when they are being pushed past each other from the side. Study the illustrations below. Compare them with the illustrations in your first two trials. Look closely at the direction of force and the direction in which the plates moved.

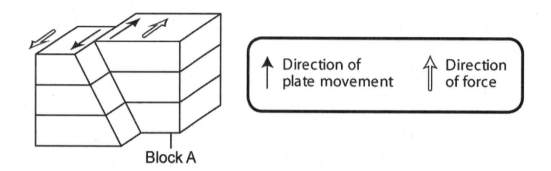

Block A

13. What type of plate boundary (divergent, convergent, transform) is typically associated with sliding or shear forces?

_____

Label each diagram below as representing a reverse, a normal, or a strike-slip fault. Then, add the appropriate arrow to show the directions of force and plate movement.

14. _____   15. _____   16. _____

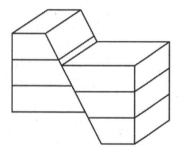
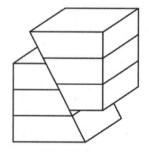
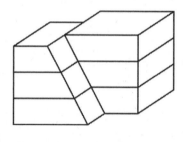

Name _____   Date _____

Lab: Plate Boundaries and Structural Geography Lesson Assessment

For the questions below, review your student's responses on the Plate Boundaries and Structural Geography Lab and input the results online.

1. Follow the procedures in the attached Modeling Folds activity to created a clay model of how forces may cause rocks to fold over time. Sketch what the fold look like on each face of your block.

2. What type of plate boundary is typically associated with pushing or compression forces?

3. Of the three main types of plate boundaries (divergent, convergent, transform), which type is most likely to be associated with pulling or tension forces?

4. What type of plate boundary (divergent, convergent, transform) is typically associated with sliding or shear forces?

5. Label each diagram below as representing a reverse, a normal, or a strike-slip fault. Then, add the appropriate arrow to show the directions of force and plate movement.

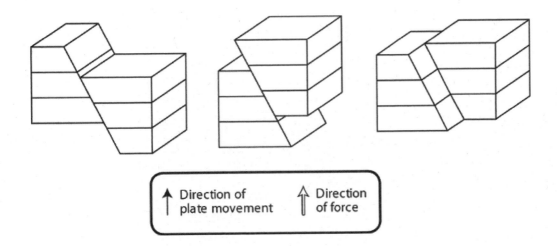

6. **Using the Geologic Map, answer the following question.**
    Sediments are almost always deposited in flat layers. Does it appear that forces in the earth affected the rock layers in this region? What clues do you have?

7. **Using the attached Geologic Map, answer the following question.**
   Did pushing (compression), pulling (tension), or sideways forces (shear) in the rock layers produce the folds and faults?

8. Look at this photograph of faulted rock layers in British Columbia, Canada. Do the rocks appear to have been pushed together, pulled apart, or to have slid past each other to make this formation? What type of fault is this?

9. Look at this photograph of a fault found in Klamath Falls, Oregon. Was the rock pulled apart, pushed together, or did it slide past another rock to make this formation? What type of fault is this?

Student Guide
Lesson 11. Optional: Your Choice

Lesson Objectives

- Practice skills and reinforce concepts taught in this course.

PREPARE

Approximate lesson time is 60 minutes.

Student Guide
Lesson 12: Earthquakes

Every year, tens of thousands of earthquakes—strong enough to be felt—occur worldwide. Most cause only a bit of shaking and maybe some minor damage. Others are deadly. On average, there are about 70–80 major earthquakes a year. Many occur in isolated areas, so they are barely noticed, except by people living near them. Occasionally, though, a major earthquake hits a large city. When that happens, it can kill or injure residents and cause devastating damage to buildings, roads, and bridges.

Lesson Objectives

- Explain causes of earthquakes.
- Explain the relationship between the speed of released energy waves in an earthquake and the material through which the waves move.
- Explain how scientists use seismic data to identify earthquake zones around the world.
- Explain how seismic data collected from earthquakes provide information about the earth's interior.

PREPARE

Approximate lesson time is 60 minutes.

Materials

For the Student

📖 Locating the Epicenter

ruler

📖 Earthquake Review

Keywords and Pronunciation

epicenter : the location on the surface of the earth directly above the focus of an earthquake

fault : a fracture in which the pieces move relative to one another

focus : the zone within the earth where rock displacement produces an earthquake

fracture (FRAK-chuhr) : a break in the rock of the earth's crust

seismic waves : compression waves caused by movements in the earth′s crust; seismic waves radiate outward from the source of an earthquake

seismogram : the record of an earthquake tremor, as recorded by a seismograph; by reading a seismogram, we can learn how powerful an earthquake is

seismograph (SIYZ-muh-graf) : an instrument used to record earthquake waves

LEARN
Activity 1: Earthquakes (Online)

Activity 2: Locating the Epicenter of an Earthquake (Online)

How can you determine the location of an earthquake epicenter? As seismologists look for patterns, they can begin to predict earthquakes and help protect people. Use the arrival times of the P waves and S waves to help you locate an epicenter and do some predicting of your own.

Locate the epicenter of an earthquake in this activity. Print the Locating the Epicenter sheet and gather the materials to begin.

Activity 3: Earthquakes (Online)

Review what you have learned about earthquakes. When finished, place your completed lesson review sheet in your Science Notebook.

ASSESS

Lesson Assessment: Earthquakes, Part 1 (*Online*)

You will complete an online assessment covering the main objectives of this lesson. Your assessment will be scored by the computer.

Lesson Assessment: Earthquakes, Part 2 (*Offline*)

You will complete an offline assessment covering the main objectives of this lesson. Your learning coach will score this assessment.

Name _____   Date _____

Locating the Epicenter of an Earthquake

Materials

ruler

Introduction

All over the earth, seismographic stations keep their instruments operating all the time. By timing the arrival of P waves and S waves, scientists at each station can tell how far their station is from the source of any earthquake.

That distance is used as the radius of a circle around the station on a map of the world. The radius is the distance from the center of the circle to any point on the circle. By comparing the distance from several stations, seismologists can locate the earthquake's epicenter.

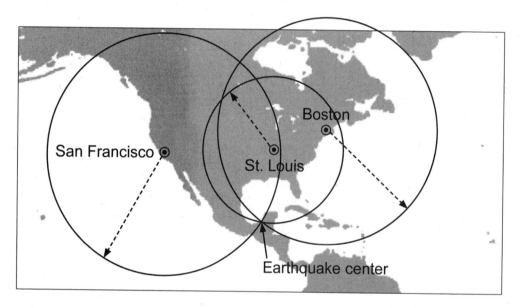

Look at the map. Notice that the three circles overlap. The location where they overlap is the approximate epicenter of the earthquake.

Procedure

1. Find the length of the radius of each circle. To calculate the radius, multiply the distance from the epicenter by 2, and then divide by 1,000 km.

Seismograph records were obtained from an earthquake in Central America. Using the information in the table, locate the epicenter on the map. You will need a compass and ruler. On this map, 1 cm is equal to 1,000 km.

Location of Station	Time Between Arrival of P and S Waves	Approximate Distance from Epicenter	Length of Radius of Circle (in cm)
Buenos Aires	1 min, 50 sec	1,600 km	
Lima	3 min, 45 sec	2,400 km	
Brasilia	4 min, 5 sec	2,880 km	

1. What city is near the epicenter?

   _____

2. List the properties of P waves and S waves.

   _____

   _____

   _____

   _____

3. What conclusion would you draw if a seismogram from a particular seismic station showed only P waves?

   _____

4. Why is it better to use data from three or more seismic stations to find the epicenter of an earthquake?

   _____

   _____

   _____

   _____

Name _____   Date _____

Earthquakes Lesson Review

Answer each question.

1. Fill in the illustration using the terms *epicenter*, *focus*, and *seismic wave*.

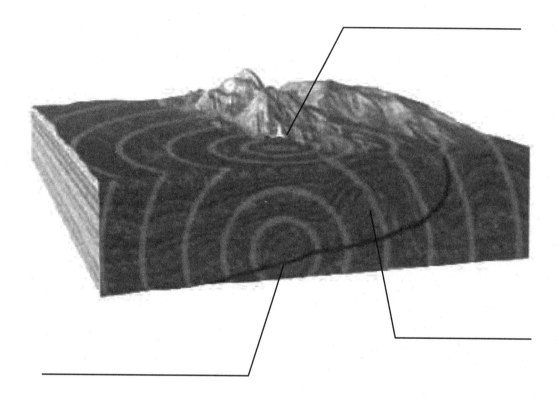

2. What causes an earthquake?

    _____

    _____

3. How is the epicenter of an earthquake related to its focus?

    _____

    _____

4. How is energy from an earthquake carried to places far from its source?

    _____

    _____

5. Imagine that this earthquake occurred because the two parts of rock on either side of the fault were being pushed together. What kind of fault is this?

    _____

Earthquakes, Part 2 Lesson Assessment

1. How did scientists use seismic data to find out about the outer core of the earth?

   _____

   _____

   _____

2. When studying seismic records from all over the globe, what did scientists find out about the pattern of earthquakes?

   _____

   _____

   _____

Student Guide
Lesson 13: LAB: Using Seismographs

Measuring seismic waves gives us clues to what lies deep inside the earth. Explore the principles behind a seismograph. Construct a simple instrument on your own. Try your hand at earthquake engineering by constructing buildings to withstand the most forceful shakes.

Lesson Objectives

- Construct a seismograph and explain how this device can detect earthquakes and other movements in the lithosphere.
- Analyze the importance of construction material and building shape in determining a building's performance and stability during an earthquake.

PREPARE

Approximate lesson time is 60 minutes.

Advance Preparation

- **Constructing a Seismograph**

- You may need several days to gather materials for this activity. Use the list below to figure out what you need.

- woodblock, approximately 20 cm x 10 cm x 4 cm

- yarn or string

- ink marker

- graph paper (10 pages)

- scissors

- table you can shake for testing (shake table)

- tape

- **Using a Seismograph in Earthquake Engineering**
- You may need several days to gather materials for this activity. A list of them are below so you can check off what you have and identify what you need.
- pipe cleaners
- brass fasteners
- craft sticks
- clay
- foam meat tray
- tape or tacks
- a table you can safely shake
- cardboard/paper pieces
- tape
- sugar cubes (1 box)
- mortar-like material: peanut butter, frosting, or double-sided tape
- cardboard
- window screen scraps (or other mesh material such as bags often used to hold produce).

Materials

For the Student

　🖳 Construct a Seismograph

marker

block, wooden

graph paper

scissors

string

table

tape - masking

　🖳 Earthquake Data Table

clay, modeling

cardboard

craft sticks

fastener, brass

foam tray

mortar-like material

pipe cleaners

seismograph

sugar cubes

window screen scraps

LEARN
Activity 1: Earthquake *(Online)*

Activity 2: Constructing a Seismograph *(Online)*
Scientists have built sophisticated seismographs that can detect the smallest movements in the lithosphere. These high-tech tools contain four main parts: a base, a pendulum, a pen, and paper. Explore the parts of a seismograph and how they work to measure seismic waves.

Read the following screens to learn about seismographs, and then print the Construct a Seismograph sheet. Finally, gather your materials and begin.

Activity 3: Earthquakes Cause Structural Damage *(Online)*

Activity 4: Using a Seismograph in Earthquake Engineering *(Offline)*
Introduction
Careful planning is required when constructing any building in an area where earthquakes are a danger. Certain factors affect how structures perform during an earthquake such as:

- The shape of the building. A building could be shaped like a rectangle, a square, an L, a T, a U, an H, a plus sign (+), an O, or a combination of these. Some buildings collapse due to "shape failure."
- The materials used to make the building - steel, concrete, wood, and brick. Steel and aluminum perform better than brittle materials such as brick.
- The height of the building. Taller buildings shake at different frequencies than shorter buildings.
- The building's foundation. Soil under a building affects its stability. So does the topography of the region.
- The number of earthquakes the building already experienced.
- The building's purpose (hospital, office, fire station).
- The building's closeness to other buildings affects its ability to withstand an earthquake.
- Characteristics of the earthquake itself, such as the earthquake's magnitude, duration, and direction and frequency of shaking, affect a building's performance.

Part 1: Wood Frame Buildings
Materials
craft sticks
clay
foam meat tray
shake table
tape or tacks
seismograph (from activity 2: Constructing a Seismograph)
Earthquake Data Table
Procedure
1. Find a partner to help you take seismograph readings.

2. Construct a square building (two or three levels high) by using the craft sticks and clay for joints.

3. Cut the tray to the same size as the outside perimeter of the building. Make a cutout for a basement.

4. Tape the building to the meat tray.

5. Tape the meat tray to the table.

6. Shake the table to simulate an earthquake. Start gently, and then shake harder. Shake back and forth to make the seismograph move up and down on the paper.

7. Stop when the building has been damaged, including any movement on the meat tray (its foundation).

8. Label the seismogram so you remember which building you tested.

9. Analyze the seismogram and write some observations about how the wood-framed buildings performed during the earthquake. Write them in the Earthquake Data Table.

Now you will stabilize your building with something called cross bracing.

10. Use the craft sticks and tape to make X-shaped braces against the inside of each wall. Use clay to secure them to the walls.

11. Shake the table again until you notice any earthquake damage. Label your seismogram so you remember which building you tested. Do you see any differences?

12. Write some observations of the cross-braced building's performance in the Earthquake Data Table.

Part 2: Brick, Stone, or Adobe Buildings

Materials

sugar cubes (1 box)

mortar-like material: peanut butter, frosting, or double-sided tape

cardboard

foam meat tray

shake table

screen scraps (from a window screen or other mesh-like material such as a produce bag)

seismograph (from activity 2: Constructing a Seismograph)

Earthquake Data Table

Procedure

1. Using sugar cubes and mortar-like material, construct four brick-like buildings: a one-story rectangular building, a one-story L-shaped building, a two-story rectangular building, a two-story L-shaped building

2. Create a cardboard floor and roof for each building and secure it with mortar.

3. Tape the meat tray to the table.

4. Test each building on the shake table. Tape the test building to the meat tray.

5. Shake the tables as before, starting gently, and then harder.

6. Stop when your building has been damaged. This includes any movement on its foundation.

7. Label the seismogram so you remember which building you tested.

8. Analyze the seismogram and write some observations about how the "brick" building performed during the earthquake. Write them in the Earthquake Data Table.

9. Write some observations of all four buildings' performances in the Earthquake Data Table. Which were more stable, one- or two-story buildings? How did the right angle in the L-shaped building affect its stability? Now you will try to construct a building in a different shape.

10. With sugar cubes and mortar, construct a new building in one of these shapes: T, U, H, +, or O. Tape it to the meat tray.

11. Simulate an earthquake as before.

12. Label the seismogram so you remember which building you tested.

13. Analyze the seismogram and write some observations about how the new shaped building performed during the earthquake. Write them in the Earthquake Data Table.

Now you will stabilize one of your buildings by turning it into a reinforced masonry structure. Cut pieces of screen smaller than the size of each wall.

14. Spread a very thin layer of peanut butter or frosting on each screen, and then carefully attach the screen to each of the inside walls of the first story.

15. Use extra peanut butter to reinforce the corners of the buildings from inside.

16. Simulate an earthquake again and analyze your seismogram. Label your seismogram so you remember which building you tested. Do you see any differences?

17. Write some observations of your stabilized building's performance in the Earthquake Data Table.

Part 3: Steel Frame Buildings

Materials

pipe cleaners

brass fasteners

foam meat tray

shake table

cardboard/paper pieces

tape

seismograph

Earthquake Data Table

Procedure

1. Use the pipe cleaners to construct a model of a modern, high-rise, steel-framed, city building.

2. Bend the end of one pipe cleaner over the other to attach them, but do not twist the ends together.

3. Attach the model to the foam tray using brass fasteners. Tape the tray to the shake table.

4. Test the building on the shake table. Start gently, and then shake harder.

5. Stop when the building has been damaged, including any movement on the foam tray (its foundation).

6. Analyze the seismogram to see how the building performed. Label your seismogram so you remember which building you tested.

7. Analyze the seismogram and write some observations about how the steel-framed building's performed during the earthquake. Write them in the Earthquake Data Table.

ASSESS

Lesson Assessment: LAB: Using Seismographs (*Online*)

Have an adult review your answers to the Using Seismographs Lab and input the results online.

Name _____   Date _____

Earthquake Data Table

Performance		
Wood	**Alone**	**After Stabilizing**
Brick and Mortar / **1 story**		
2 story		
1-story L		
2-story L		
Other shape		
Steel		

Name _____   Date _____

Application:

Compare the seismograph readings for each test. Think about what you observed about each building. Decide which structural shape performs best during an earthquake. Decide which building materials perform best during an earthquake: ductile materials, such as steel and aluminum, or brittle materials, such as brick and stone?

Write your conclusions below. Include the following information:

- Which building shapes perform best during an earthquake? How did you learn this from your tests?

- Which building materials perform best during an earthquake? How did you learn this from your tests?

- Look at the photos of buildings that show earthquake damage. Choose three photos and make recommendations for how the buildings could have been made more "earthquake-proof."

_____

_____

_____

_____

_____

_____

_____

_____

_____

_____

_____

_____

_____

_____

Name _____   Date _____

Construct a Seismograph

Materials

woodblock, approximately 20 cm x 10 cm x 4 cm

yarn or string

ink marker

graph paper (10 pages)

scissors

table you can shake for testing (shake table)

tape

Procedure

1. Find a table you can shake quite forcefully. Clear it of any items, and then place it in an area with plenty of space.

2. Trim the edges from the centimeter grid paper. Cut the remaining grid in half so that you have two strips 10 squares wide. Repeat for each piece of paper.

3. Make one long strip by taping each small strip at the short end.

4. Tie one end of the yarn to the wood block so the block hangs with the short side down.

5. Remove the cap from the marker. Tape the marker to the block so the tip hangs off the bottom edge.

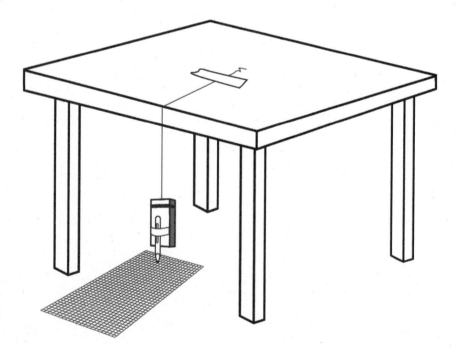

Name _____   Date _____

6. Place your paper strip under the table, grid side up. Slide the paper underneath the table so you can pull the starting edge of the strip from underneath.

7. Hang the block and marker over the long edge of the table so the tip of the marker just barely touches the paper. The block should swing freely, but the marker tip should touch the paper.

8. Work with a partner. One person should stand at the short end of the table and shake the table back and forth. A second person should kneel on the floor and pull the paper through the table.

9. Start slowly. Shake the table lightly and then build up to faster, stronger shakes.

Watch your seismogram appear as you simulate an earthquake. Compare the recordings of the slow vibrations to the quick, strong ones. You will need your seismograph for the rest of the lesson.

Name _____   Date _____

Lab: Using Seismographs Lesson Assessment

For the questions below, review your student's responses on the Using Seismographs Lab and input the results online.

1. Follow the procedures in the attached Construct a Seismograph activity and, using the information gathered during the experiments, complete the Earthquake Data Table.

2. Based on the data recorded in your Earthquake Data Table, complete the Application section of the attached Earthquake Data Table.

Student Guide
Lesson 14: Unit Review

The earth is constantly shifting: mountains can become beaches, continents can move apart and oceans fill in between them, and volcanoes can erupt because of changes that happen inside the earth. How do we know that this is so? Before your unit assessment, let's review what you have learned about the theories and evidence that helped scientists explain earth's changing surface.

Lesson Objectives

- Describe the names, locations, and main characteristics of the layers that make up earth's interior.
- Recognize that movements in the earth's crust create seismic waves that scientists study to learn about earth's interior.
- Explain the historical development of the theory of continental drift.
- Describe evidence that supported the theory of continental drift.
- Describe key features of the theory of plate tectonics.
- Describe observations that the theory of plate tectonics explained what the theory of continental drift did not explain as well.
- Relate motion at the boundaries of earth's plates to the formation of landforms and geologic events.

PREPARE

Approximate lesson time is 60 minutes.

Keywords and Pronunciation

Theory of Continental Drift : the theory that the continents were previously joined together, and over time broke up and slowly drifted apart to their present positions

asthenosphere (as-THE-nuh-sfir) : the upper part of the earth´s mantle

compression : stress on a material from a force or forces pushing inward from one or both ends

convection (kuhn-VEK-shuhn) : the transfer of heat by the circulation or movement of the heated parts of a liquid or gas

convergent plate boundary : a boundary at which tectonic plates are moving toward one another or colliding

convergent plates : plates that are moving toward one another

crust : the outermost, solid layer of any planet or moon

divergent plate boundary : a plate boundary where two plates move away from each other

epicenter : the location on the surface of the earth directly above the focus of an earthquake

hot spot : a hot place in the mantle where magma rises, often melting the crust above to form a volcano

magma : the molten or partly molten mixture of minerals, gases, and melted rock found below the earth´s surface

ridge push : at a divergent boundary, the pushing force on a tectonic plate caused by gravity acting on its elevated edge

San Andreas (san an-DRAY-uhs)

seismic waves : compression waves caused by movements in the earth´s crust; seismic waves radiate outward from the source of an earthquake

seismogram : the record of an earthquake tremor, as recorded by a seismograph; by reading a seismogram, we can learn how powerful an earthquake is

seismograph (SIYZ-muh-graf) : an instrument used to record earthquake waves

slab pull : at a convergent boundary, the pulling force on a tectonic plate that causes its edge to sink into the mantle

subduction (suhb-DUHK-shuhn)

tension : stress on a material from a force or forces pulling outward from one or both ends

Theory of Plate Tectonics : the scientific theory that earth's crust is made up of about 20 huge plates that are always moving very slowly. According to the Theory of Plate Tectonics, all seven continents were once part of a super continent called Pangaea.

transform plate boundaries : a plate boundary where two plates move in opposite directions alongside one another

---

LEARN
Activity 1: Plate Tectonics *(Online)*

Student Guide
Lesson 15: Unit Assessment

You have learned a lot about plates, landforms, and plate activities. Now you are ready to take the unit assessment. It is time to show all the knowledge that you have acquired.

Lesson Objectives

- Describe the names, locations, and main characteristics of the layers that make up earth's interior.
- Recognize that movements in the earth's crust create seismic waves that scientists study to learn about earth's interior.
- Describe key features of the theory of plate tectonics.
- Relate motion at the boundaries of earth's plates to the formation of landforms and geologic events.
- Describe key features of the theory of plate tectonics.
- Explain the historical development of the theory of continental drift.
- Describe evidence that supported the theory of continental drift.

PREPARE

Approximate lesson time is 60 minutes.

ASSESS

Unit Assessment: Plate Tectonics, Part 1 (*Online*)

You will complete an online assessment of the main objectives covered so far in this unit. Follow the instructions online. Your assessment will be scored by the computer.

Unit Assessment: Plate Tectonics, Part 2 (*Offline*)

Complete the offline part of the Unit Assessment. Your learning coach will score this part of the Assessment.

Student Guide
Lesson 1. Optional: Your Choice

Have you ever noticed how much everyday life is affected by the weather? Rain and sunshine can affect our moods. Snow and ice can cause cities to shut down. Worse yet – humidity can be disastrous for our hair! In this unit, you will explore the many factors involved in producing everyday weather. Learn how the atmosphere provides protection and explore climates all over the world.

Lesson Objectives

- Practice skills and reinforce concepts taught in this course.

PREPARE

Approximate lesson time is 60 minutes.

Student Guide
Lesson 2: Layers of the Atmosphere

Spacecrafts traveling around earth often take pictures of our planet from space. In the picture on-screen, you can see a thin, blue layer wrapped like a blanket around the earth.

Life on earth depends on the gases in this layer. Earth's gravity holds this layer close to the planet. Beyond this layer, lies the cold darkness of space. What's this layer about?

Lesson Objectives

- Identify the layers of the atmosphere.
- Describe the major components that make up earth's atmosphere.
- Describe the interaction of altitude, air density, air pressure, and temperature in the atmosphere.

PREPARE

Approximate lesson time is 60 minutes.

Advance Preparation

- If you don't already have it, please gather 2 large round balloons and a measuring tape.

Materials

    For the Student

        🖳 Investigating Temperature and Density

        advanced thermometer

        ice

        large bowl or pot

        large round balloon (2)

        measuring tape

        water

Keywords and Pronunciation

air : a mixture of nitrogen, oxygen, and small amounts of other gases that surrounds the earth and forms its atmosphere

air pressure : the result of the weight of air in the atmosphere pressing down on earth

altitude : the height of an object above the surface of the earth

atmosphere : a blanket of gases that surrounds earth and certain other planets

aurora : streamers or bands of light sometimes visible in the night sky in northern or southern regions of the earth; scientists think an aurora is caused by charged particles from the sun that enter the earth's magnetic field and stimulate molecules in the atmosphere

chlorofluorocarbon (KLOR-oh-flor-oh-KAHR-buhn) : any of several compounds of carbon, fluorine, chlorine, and hydrogen: used as refrigerants, foam-blowing agents, solvents, and in aerosol cans until scientists became concerned about depletion of the atmospheric ozone layer

density : the concentration of matter in an object or part of an object

exosphere (EK-soh-sfeer) : the top layer of the thermosphere

---

fluctuate (FLUHK-choo-eyt) : to shift back and forth

ionosphere (ahy-ON-uh-sfeer) : the region of the earth's atmosphere between the stratosphere and the exosphere

mesosphere (MEZ-uh-sfeer) : a layer of the atmosphere between the stratosphere and thermosphere, which lies between 50 and 80 kilometers (30 to 50 miles) above the surface of the earth

ozone (OH-zohn) : a form of oxygen which, in a layer in the stratosphere, screens out harmful ultraviolet rays from the sun

stratosphere : a layer of the atmosphere above the troposphere where temperature rises slightly with altitude

thermosphere : the topmost layer of the earth's atmosphere that begins about 80 kilometers (50 miles) above the earth's surface and extends into space

troposphere (TROH-puh-sfihr) : the atmospheric layer closest to the surface of the earth, which extends from the ground to between about 9 and 18 kilometers (6 and 11 miles) above the surface

---

LEARN
Activity 1: Layers of the Atmosphere *(Online)*

Activity 2: Investigating Air Pressure and Temperature *(Offline)*
When scientists need to study something that happens too slowly, too quickly, or something that is too difficult to be observed, they use a model. In this activity, you will use a model to understand temperature and air pressure in the atmosphere.

ASSESS
Lesson Assessment: Layers of the Atmosphere, Part 1 (*Online*)
You will complete an online assessment covering the main objectives of this lesson. Your assessment will be scored by the computer.

Lesson Assessment: Layers of the Atmosphere, Part 2 (*Offline*)
You will complete an offline assessment covering the main objectives of this lesson. Your learning coach will score this assessment.

Name _____   Date _____

Investigating Temperature and Density

Atmospheric layers can be described by their altitude, density, temperature, and air pressure. In this activity, see how changes in temperature affect air density.

Materials

round balloon, 2

measuring tape

thermometer

ice

pot or bowl, large

water

Hypothesis

In this investigation, you will see how temperature affects air density in two balloons. Predict what will happen when one balloon is cooled in ice and the other is not. Why?

_____

_____

_____

Procedure

1. Blow up two balloons to the same size and tie them shut. Make sure they will be able to fit in the pot.

2. Use the measuring tape to measure the circumference (distance around the center) of both balloons. Record your measurements in cm in the data table.

3. Read the temperature of the thermometer. Record the temperature in °C next to "Starting temperature" for both balloons in the data table.

4. Fill the pot with ice and cold water to create an ice bath. Place one balloon and the thermometer into an ice bath for 10 minutes. Let the other balloon stay at room temperature.

5. After 10 minutes read the temperature of the thermometer in the ice bath. Record the temperature in the data table. Record the room temperature from your measurement in step 3.

6. Take the balloon and thermometer out of the ice bath.

7. Immediately measure the circumference of each balloon. Record the circumference in the data table.

8. Let both balloons stay at room temperature for five minutes. Observe both balloons.

9. Measure the circumference of each balloon again after five minutes. Record your measurements in the data table.

	Balloon 1: No ice bath	Balloon 2: Ice bath
Starting circumference		
Starting temperature		
Temperature after 10 minutes in ice		
Circumference after 10 minutes in ice		
Temperature after 5 minutes at room temperature		
Circumference after 5 minutes at room temperature		

Analysis

1. Describe what happened to the temperature and circumference of the balloon in the ice bath.

   _____

2. Did any air escape from the balloon in the ice bath?

   _____

3. Did the density of the air in the balloon increase or decrease because of cooling? Explain.

   _____

   _____

Conclusion

In this activity, you used a model to understand how temperature and density interact. The air in this experiment had equal amounts of air pressure.

In what way does the experiment model atmospheric layers?

_____

_____

In what ways does the experiment **not** model atmospheric layers?

_____

_____

Name _____ Date _____

Layers of the Atmosphere,
Part 2 Lesson Assessment

Directions: Answer the questions below.

(10 points)

1. In the space below, draw a diagram of the atmosphere labeling the stratosphere, troposphere, mesosphere, and thermosphere.

(10 points)

2. Describe the change in air pressure and density as altitude increases in the atmosphere.

_____

_____

(10 points)

3. Describe how temperature fluctuates through the layers of the atmosphere.

_____

_____

_____

_____

Student Guide
Lesson 3: Conduction, Convection, and Radiation

What do a mood ring, a lava light, and a space heater have in common with earth's weather? Find out by learning how three kinds of heat transfer are related to weather on earth.

Lesson Objectives

- Recognize that earth's heat energy (thermal energy) is distributed by convection, conduction, and radiation.
- Explain how heat energy is transferred from warmer to cooler places (in the air, water, and on land).

PREPARE

Approximate lesson time is 60 minutes.

Materials

For the Student

- Graph Paper

  lamp - gooseneck

  sand - 240 mL

  stopwatch

  advanced thermometer

  cups, paper - 12 oz (2)

  cylinder, graduated

  safety goggles

  water - 240 mL

Keywords and Pronunciation

conduction : the transfer of heat between two adjoining objects, caused by a temperature difference between the objects

convection (kuhn-VEK-shuhn) : the transfer of heat by the circulation or movement of the heated parts of a liquid or gas

electromagnetic radiation (ih-LEK-troh-mag-NEH-tik) : radiation consisting of electromagnetic waves, including radio waves, infrared, visible light, ultraviolet, X rays, and gamma rays

infrared (in-frah-RED) : radiation that lies outside the visible spectrum of light at its red end and has a wavelength between about 700 nanometers and 1 millimeter

radiation : the process in which energy is emitted by one body, transmitted through an intervening medium or space, and absorbed by another body

LEARN
Activity 1: Conduction, Convection, and Radiation *(Online)*

Activity 2: Heat Race *(Offline)*
Heat Race

Air above the ground heats differently from the air above the ocean. In this activity, you will model one way that heat is transferred on earth to find out more about these differences.

Hypothesis
Hypothesize which will warm up faster, the sand or the water.

_____

_____

Materials
colored pencils
cups, paper - 2, 12 oz.
graduated cylinder
lamp - gooseneck
sand - 240 ml
stopwatch
thermometer
water - 240 ml

Procedure
1. In your Science Notebook, make a data table with spaces to record the temperature of a cup of water and a cup of sand every 2 minutes for 10 minutes. Put this table in the data section below.
2. Use the graduated cylinder to measure and fill one cup with 240 mL sand.
3. Use the graduated cylinder to measure and fill the other cup with 240 mL water.
4. Stick the thermometer about 5 mm into the sand and wait 60 seconds for it to settle. Record the temperature in your data table next to 0 minutes.
5. Place a lamp 15 cm above the cup with sand.
6. Place the thermometer in the sand.
7. Check the temperature of the sand every 2 minutes for 10 minutes. Use the stopwatch to keep time.
8. Each time you check the temperature, record it in the data table.
9. Remove the thermometer and allow it to return to room temperature.
Repeat steps 4–9 for the cup of water. Make sure the thermometer is in the water to the same depth as it was for the sand. You may need to hold it there or make a way to have it held in place.

Data Table
Follow step 1 in the procedure section to make a data table in your Science Notebook.

Analysis
1. Using the graph paper, make a line graph comparing the changes in temperature over time for both the water and the sand.
2. Choose one color to graph sand temperature and another to graph water temperature.

3. Start with your sand temperature observations. Make a point above 0 minutes at the temperature you recorded for the sand.

4. Make points for your observations at every 2 minutes in the test.

5. Use a ruler to connect the points on the graph.

6. Use a different color and repeat steps 2–4 for water.

Conclusion

Answer the questions below. Refer to the lesson if you need to.

1. What differences did you notice in the rate of heating between the sand and the water?

_____

_____

_____

2. What reasons could you give for the different rates of heating of sand and water? Use the term molecules in your answer.

_____

_____

_____

3. Which kind of heat transfer were you modeling when you placed the lamp over the sand and water?

_____

_____

_____

4. How is this kind of heat transfer different from the other two types you studied in this lesson?

_____

_____

_____

5. Use one kind of heat transfer to explain why seaside towns often have cooler temperatures than inland areas.

_____

_____

_____

ASSESS

Lesson Assessment: Conduction, Convection, and Radiation, Part 1 (*Online*)

You will complete an online assessment covering the main objectives of this lesson. Your assessment will be scored by the computer.

Lesson Assessment: Conduction, Convection, and Radiation, Part 2 (*Offline*)

You will complete an offline assessment covering the main objectives of this lesson. Your learning coach will score this assessment.

Name _____   Date _____

Graph Paper

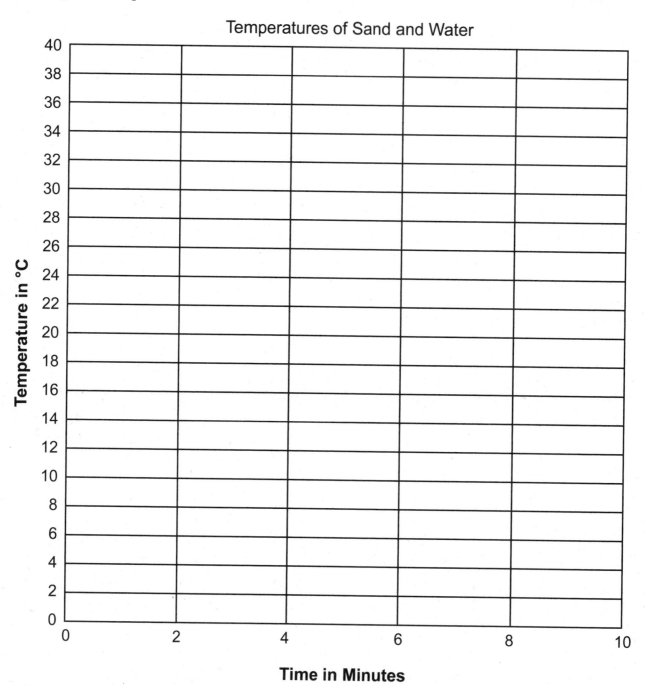

Temperatures of Sand and Water

Name _____   Date _____

Conduction, Convection, and Radiation, Part 2 Lesson Assessment

Directions: Answer the questions below.

1. What does heat have to do with the circular movement of air in the atmosphere? Explain. You may draw a picture with your explanation.

_____

_____

_____

2. In the lesson activity Heat Race, how was conduction involved in the different temperatures of the sand and the water? Explain. You may draw a picture with your explanation.

_____

_____

Student Guide
Lesson 4: Daily Weather

Like it or dislike it, we all live with weather. Explore the four main factors that create weather: temperature, humidity, air pressure, and wind.

Lesson Objectives

- Define weather as the physical conditions of the atmosphere at a given location and time, as described by temperature, wind, air pressure, and humidity.

PREPARE

Approximate lesson time is 60 minutes.

Advance Preparation

- This activity takes place over a three-day period, but should not be started until the same day as the lesson.

Materials

For the Student

    🖥 Accurate Weather Reports

       newspaper - local

       newspaper - national

       radio

       telephone

       television

       websites

Keywords and Pronunciation

condensation : the process by which water vapor changes from gas to liquid

dew point : the temperature at which the water vapor in the air would begin to condense to liquid, if the air were cooled to that temperature

humidity : the amount of water vapor in a given volume of air

precipitation : moisture, such as rain, snow, sleet, and hail, that falls from the atmosphere to the earth

relative humidity : the amount of water vapor in the air divided by the amount that would have to be present in the same air to form a cloud or condense on a surface

weather : the day-to-day conditions of an area, including the temperature, wind direction and speed, air pressure, relative humidity, and precipitation

LEARN
Activity 1: Daily Weather *(Online)*

Activity 2: Where Can I Get an Accurate Weather Report? *(Offline)*

Activity 3: Daily Weather *(Offline)*
Weather Analogies
Review what you have learned about weather. When finished, place your completed lesson review sheet in your Science Notebook.
Directions
Below are related pairs of words or phrases. Write the word that best completes the second pair to match the relationship expressed in the first pair. An example is done for you.

Example: evaporation : water vapor :: condensation : **liquid water**

1. low density : low pressure :: high density : _____
2. low pressure : rainy :: high pressure : _____
3. high temperature : high humidity :: low temperature : _____
4. condensation : clouds :: precipitation : _____
5. solar energy : radiation :: wind : _____
6. cooling : contract :: heating : _____
7. hot air : rises :: cool air : _____
8. air : air molecule :: water : _____
9. high humidity : low air pressure :: low humidity : _____

ASSESS

Lesson Assessment: Daily Weather, Part 1 *(Online)*
You will complete an online assessment covering the main objectives of this lesson. Your assessment will be scored by the computer.

Lesson Assessment: Daily Weather, Part 2 *(Offline)*
You will complete an offline assessment covering the main objectives of this lesson. Your learning coach will score this assessment.

Name _____ Date _____

Accurate Weather Reports

A weather report is a description of weather for one day. A weather forecast is a prediction of weather in the future. What does a weather report contain? Each day, weather reports are available to you on the television, radio, newspaper, and the Internet. In this activity, you will compare weather forecasts from three sources and decide which is most accurate.

Hypothesis

Choose three sources from the list below. Of these three, which do you predict will give the most accurate weather description?

_____

_____

Materials

radio
television
local newspaper
national newspaper
phone
weather websites: www.weather.com, www.noaa.com

Procedure

1. Check each of your three sources for a report of today's weather. Record the information in Data Table 1.

2. Check each source for weather forecasts over the next three days. Record the information in Data Table 2.

3. Over the next three days, record the actual weather in Data Table 2.

4. If you need more room to record the weather, recopy the data tables into your Science Notebook.

Data Table 1

Today's Weather

Weather report source	Temperature	Wind speed	Relative humidity	Air pressure (high or low)	Precipitation

Data Table 2

Weather Forecasts over Three-Day Period

Weather report source	Day 1 Forecast	Day 1 Actual Weather	Day 2 Forecast	Day 2 Actual Weather	Day 3 Forecast	Day 3 Actual Weather

Analyzing the Data:

1. Look over the information in your table carefully. Compare the predicted weather with the actual weather.

2. Rank the weather sources from most accurate (1) to least accurate (3).

3. Explain why you ranked the weather report sources the way you did.

_____

_____

Conclusion

1. Which kind of weather report has the most information? Is this related to the type of report? Explain.

_____

2. What information do all of the reports include? Why is that information included in every weather report?

_____

_____

3. Why does the accuracy of weather forecasts usually decrease as the number of days ahead increases?

_____

4. What question did you explore in this activity? Can you answer that question now? How come?

_____

_____

_____

Name _____   Date _____

Daily Weather, Part 2 Lesson Assessment

Weather is a result of temperature differences all over earth. In the spaces below, explain how temperature is related to the following weather traits.

1. wind:

_____

_____

2. humidity:

_____

_____

3. air pressure:

_____

_____

Student Guide
Lesson 5: Air Circulation

Depending on where you live on earth, you may consider the wind a friend or an enemy. Either way, the wind will keep blowing and its pattern will probably not change anytime soon. Explore how air pressure is related to wind and learn about the differences in wind speed between two American towns.

Lesson Objectives
- Describe the effect of earth's rotation on air circulation patterns.
- Define wind as the horizontal movement of air.
- Recognize that air moves from areas of higher pressure to areas of lower pressure.

PREPARE

Approximate lesson time is 60 minutes.

Materials
> For the Student
>> 🖳 Isobar Map
>> 🖳 Working With Scientific Data: Isobars
>
> markers or crayons

Keywords and Pronunciation
air pressure gradient : the change in air pressure over a given distance
Coriolis effect (kor-ee-OH-luhs) : the curved movement of air or water caused by the rotation of the earth
friction : a force that resists motion between two objects that are in contact
isobar (IY-suh-bahr) : line on a weather map that connects areas of equal air pressure

LEARN
Activity 1: Air Circulation *(Online)*

Activity 2: Working With Scientific Data: Isobars *(Offline)*
What's the difference between "high" and "low"? Work with scientific data to understand how pressure is measured and displayed on a weather map.

ASSESS

Lesson Assessment: Air Circulation, Part 1 (*Online*)
You will complete an online assessment covering the main objectives of this lesson. Your assessment will be scored by the computer.

Lesson Assessment: Air Circulation, Part 2 (*Offline*)
You will complete an offline assessment covering the main objectives of this lesson. Your learning coach will score this assessment.

Name _____   Date _____

Isobar Map

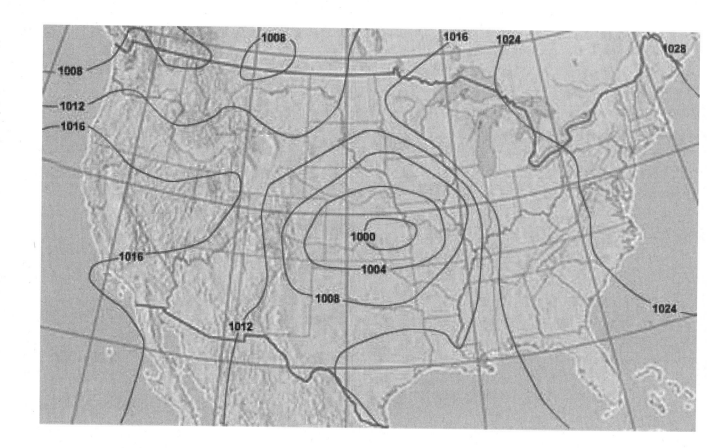

Name _____ Date _____

Working with Scientific Data: Isobars

Low- and high-pressure areas are important in understanding weather patterns. High-pressure regions are usually associated with dry weather because as the air sinks it warms and the moisture evaporates. Low-pressure regions usually bring precipitation because when the air rises it cools and the water vapor condenses.

Isobars

To see where areas of low and high pressure are, meteorologists draw lines on maps connecting places where pressures are the same. These lines are called *isobars*, meaning "equal pressure" lines.

Isobars show patterns of air pressure across wide areas. The lines form curves encircling the area. Isobars can also show us where pressure changes are small or large over a certain distance. The area around Illinois is probably windy because there is a quick change of pressure over a small area.

A special instrument called a *barometer* measures air pressure in millibars. On the sample map below you can see isobars drawn every 4 millibars.

Sample Map

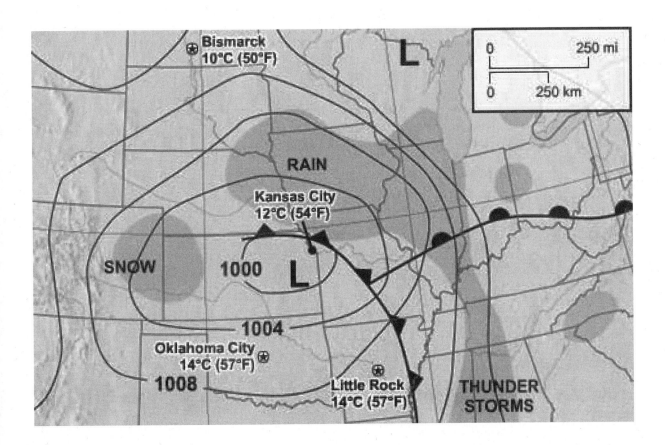

Isobar Data

Study the isobar map.

1. Label high-pressure areas with the letter "H."

2. Label low-pressure areas with the letter "L."

3. Over which area(s) would you expect to see rain or snow?

    _____

    _____

4. Over which area(s) would you expect to see clear skies?

    _____

    _____

In the Northern Hemisphere the wind blows clockwise around centers of high pressure. The wind blows counterclockwise around lows. It is the opposite in the Southern Hemisphere.

5. Draw arrows around the "H" on your map to show the wind direction.

6. Draw arrows around the "L" on your map to show the wind direction.

7. Imagine that you live in Maine. Currently there is a high-pressure area over Maine. If a low-pressure area moves in, how will the direction of the wind change?

    _____

    _____

8. Imagine that you live in Colorado. Currently there is a low-pressure area over Colorado. If a high-pressure area moves in, how will the direction of the wind change?

    _____

    _____

Challenge

9. Based on what you learned in this lesson where would you expect the strongest winds? Refer to the lesson if you need to.

    _____

Name _____   Date _____

Air Circulation Lesson Assessment

(10 points)

1.   In the space below, draw a simple globe. Label the poles and the equator. Then draw the routes of earth's global winds on its surface.

(10 points)

2.   Explain how earth's rotation affects the direction the wind travels from equator to pole and from pole to equator.

_____

_____

_____

_____

Student Guide
Lesson 6: Air Masses

Why is a sunny day in northern Canada so different from a sunny day in the Caribbean? Air in the lower part of earth's atmosphere is similar to the surface it is closest to. Learn more about the large bodies of air that form over earth's surface.

Lesson Objectives

- Locate and describe air masses on a weather map.
- Define an air mass as a large body of air characterized by nearly uniform temperature, humidity, and ground-level pressure.

PREPARE

Approximate lesson time is 60 minutes.

Materials

For the Student

  🖳 Air Mass Concept Map

  markers or crayons

  pencils, colored 12

  ruler

Keywords and Pronunciation

air mass : a body of air covering a relatively wide area, with about the same properties through any horizontal section

front : a zone of transition between two different kinds of air masses

maritime : of or related to the sea

polar : of or relating to the North or South Pole

LEARN
Activity 1: Air Masses *(Online)*

Activity 2: Concept Maps *(Offline)*

When working with new information, sometimes pictures can help you organize and remember information. Design a concept map to help you understand the traits of different air masses.

ASSESS

Lesson Assessment: Air Masses (*Online*)

You will complete an online assessment covering the main objectives of this lesson. Your assessment will be scored by the computer.

Name _____   Date _____

Air Mass Concept Map

Here's a riddle: what do you get when you cross a spider with a lot of new information? A concept map! (or a librarian with lots of legs).

Concept maps are a visual way of organizing information. They help you learn by showing facts "at a glance." Sometimes your brain can remember things more easily with a diagram or mental image. You've heard a picture is worth a thousand words, right? A concept map is worth at least ten-thousand.

Types of Concept Maps

What makes concept maps fun is their diversity and the different ways to show information. Take care to make sure you represent relationships correctly. Here are some examples of concept maps.

Map Description	What It Looks Like*
Spider map: The main idea is in the middle with supporting details arranged around it.	
Branching map: Big ideas appear at the top and supporting ideas are organized below.	
Flow chart: This shows the steps of a process in order.	

*You can choose whatever shapes and colors you want to use for your concept map.

Tips for Making a Concept Map

1. Gather paper, markers, and a ruler and some shapes to trace (optional).

2. Get your reference materials ready. In this activity, you will use information from your Science lessons.

3. Be familiar with the different types of concept maps so you know which one best represents this information.

4. Relax and visualize the information in your head.

5. Try sketching a diagram in pencil first.

6. You might need to draw more than one map, or think of ways to connect smaller maps to show all of the information.

7. Use colors or shapes to show differences between main ideas and supporting details.

8. Check to see that your map is clear and makes sense to you. If not, revise it!

Make the Map

Now you will make a concept map. Your concept map will organize information about four types of air masses. Use the word bank below to help you. You may want to include additional vocabulary and ideas.

Word Bank

continental	polar	tropical	maritime
humid	dry	air mass	pressure
weather	warm	temperature	cold
dense	pressure	latitude	high
low	precipitation		

1. What kind of map do you think is best to use to organize information about four kinds of air masses? Why did you choose that map?

_____

_____

_____

3. In your Science Notebook or on a piece of blank paper, begin your concept map. When finished, show your map to an adult to check your work.

4. Remember: the best map is one that makes sense to you. Your map may not look exactly like one that another person has made, but that's okay. Concept maps are helpful when you want to show important concepts and how these ideas are related.

Student Guide
Lesson 7: Weather Fronts

Has this ever happened to you while doing schoolwork? If so, you may want to pay attention to this lesson. Find out what kinds of weather different air masses can bring and next time you'll be prepared for sudden snowstorms.

Lesson Objectives

- Describe how air masses interact at cold, warm, stationary, and occluded fronts.
- Describe typical weather details associated with cold, warm, stationary, and occluded fronts.

PREPARE

Approximate lesson time is 60 minutes.

Materials

For the Student

    🖥 Exploring Fronts

Optional

    computer

Keywords and Pronunciation

cold front : the zone separating two air masses, of which the cooler, denser mass is advancing and replacing the warmer

isobar (IY-suh-bahr) : line on a weather map that connects areas of equal air pressure

occluded front (uh-KLOOD-uhd) : a front that forms when warm air is wedged upward between two cold fronts

stationary front : a front between warm and cold air masses that is moving very slowly or not at all

warm front : a transition zone between a mass of warm air and the colder air it is replacing

LEARN
Activity 1: Weather Fronts (Online)

Activity 2: Exploring Fronts (Offline)
Organize the information you have learned in this lesson about each type of front.

ASSESS

Lesson Assessment: Weather Fronts (Offline)
You will complete an offline assessment covering the main objectives of this lesson. Your learning coach will score this assessment.

Name _____   Date _____

Exploring Fronts

A table is one way to organize a lot of new information. Use the lesson and the table below to organize what you have learned about fronts. You may write into the table on this sheet or create a new table using a computer program.

Front	How Air Masses Interact	Weather
Warm		
Cold		
Stationary		
Occluded		

Name _____   Date _____

Weather Fronts Lesson Assessment

Next to each statement, fill in the type of front that is described (cold, warm, stationary, or occluded).

(2 points)

1. _____ Warm, less-dense air rises gradually above cooler air.

(2 points)

2. _____ Rainy or snowy weather lasts a very long time at this front.

(2 points)

3. _____ Denser, colder air pushes in under warm air.

(2 points)

4. _____ Weather may be drizzly or snowy.

(2 points)

5. _____ Cold and warm air are next to each other, but are at
   a standstill.

(2 points)

6. _____ Warm air is forced up in a wedge between two masses
   of cold air.

(2 points)

7. _____ This kind of air mass usually brings thunderclouds and storms.

Use the map below to answer question 8.

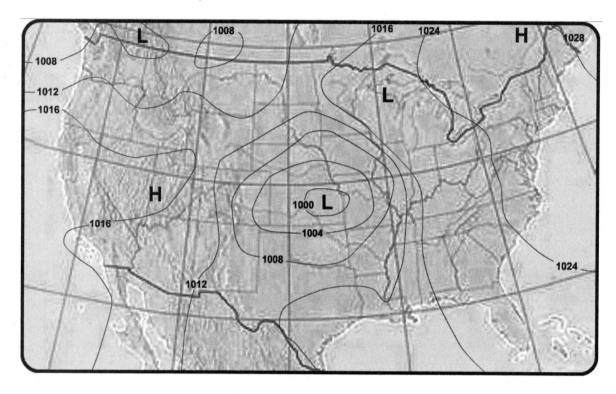

(10 points)

8. A high pressure system is sitting over the coast of Virginia in early summer. How would the weather change if a cold front moves into this area?

    _____

    _____

    _____

    _____

Student Guide
Lesson 8: Meteorology

Predicting the weather can be a challenging task of studying and understanding data. Even then weather can be unpredictable. Learn about the scientists who predict weather and their tools of the trade.

Lesson Objectives

- Given weather data for a particular location, develop a weather forecast for that area.
- Interpret weather symbols and isobars on a weather map to describe the weather in a given location.

PREPARE

Approximate lesson time is 60 minutes.

Materials

For the Student

    🖳 U.S. Weather Map

Keywords and Pronunciation

barometer (buh-RAH-muh-tuhr) : a tool used to measure air pressure

hygrometer (hiy-GRAH-muh-tuhr) : a tool used to measure the amount of humidity, or moisture, in the air

isobar (IY-suh-bahr) : line on a weather map that connects areas of equal air pressure

meteorologist (mee-tee-uh-RAH-luh-jist) : a scientist who studies weather and reports on weather conditions

---

LEARN
Activity 1: Meteorology *(Online)*

Activity 2: Investigating Weather Maps *(Offline)*

Study the United States weather map.

Imagine you are in Columbus, Ohio.

---

1. What kind of weather should you expect as the cold front arrives?

    _____

    _____

    _____

2. How will the temperature and pressure of the air change?

    _____

    _____

    _____

3. Will the air be denser after the front passes?

    _____

    _____

    _____

Imagine you are in Jackson, Mississippi.

4. As the warm front comes close, what kinds of clouds would you expect to see?

    _____

    _____

    _____

5. What kind of weather should you expect?

    _____

    _____

    _____

6. In Seattle, Washington, a cold air mass and a warm air mass are next to each other but are at a standstill. Draw the symbol for this type of front on the map near Seattle.

    _____

    _____

    _____

This weather map is for April 2, 1988. Imagine it is April 4.

7. What will the weather be as the high-pressure area moves into Denver, Colorado?

    _____

    _____

    _____

8. What kind of weather would you expect in Columbus, Ohio? Explain why and include details about fronts and air pressure.

    _____

    _____

    _____

9. Why is it hard for meteorologists to predict the exact weather every time?

    _____

    _____

ASSESS

Lesson Assessment: Meteorology (*Online*)

You will complete an online assessment covering the main objectives of this lesson. Your assessment will be scored by the computer.

Name   Date

U.S. Weather Map – April 2, 1988

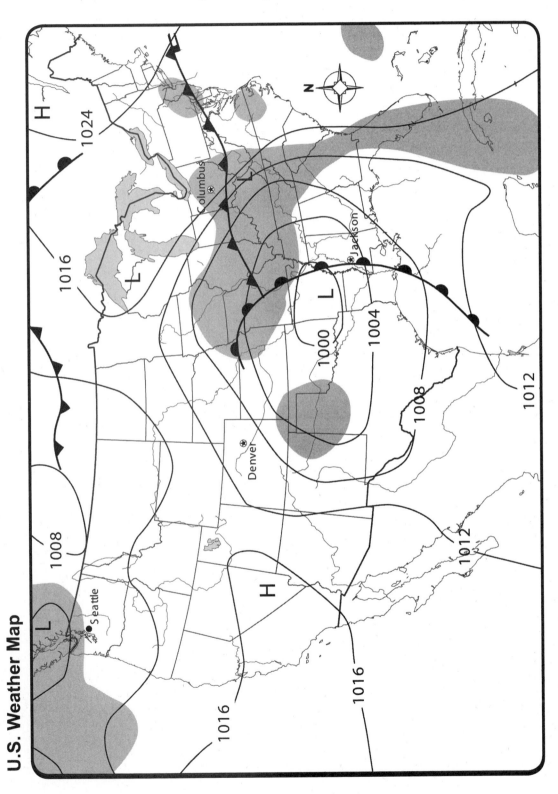

U.S. Weather Map

Student Guide
Lesson 9: LAB: Working with Weather

This lab will help you bring together the information you have learned so far about air and weather. Construct a barometer and measure air pressure. Then test your weather prediction skills by using information in a weather report to create a map and predict the weather.

Lesson Objectives
- Conduct investigations using weather measurement devices.
- Collect and use data to analyze the weather.

PREPARE

Approximate lesson time is 60 minutes.

Materials
For the Student
- 🖳 Build a Barometer
- 🖳 Graph Paper
  - drinking straw
  - jar, glass - without lid
  - large round balloon
  - rubber bands, thick
  - ruler
  - safety goggles
  - scissors
  - tape - masking
  - toothpicks
- 🖳 U.S. Weather Maps

Keywords and Pronunciation
barometer (buh-RAH-muh-tuhr) : a tool used to measure air pressure

millibar : a centimeter-gram-second unit of pressure equal to one thousandth of a bar or 1,000 dynes per square centimeter, used to measure air pressure

---

LEARN
Activity 1: Build a Barometer *(Online)*

Activity 2: Build a Barometer (Offline)

Activity 3: Working With Scientific Data: Weather Forecasting (Offline)

Working with Scientific Data: Weather Forecasting

Have you ever heard a weather report predicting snow that never arrived, or a dry day that ended in pouring rain? Even with all the data available about wind, temperature, precipitation, and air pressure, there is still some mystery about how to accurately forecast the weather. Who says that mystery can't be fun?

In this activity, you will work with some weather data to create a weather map, which is different from reading a weather map. Then you will attempt to predict the weather over a four-day period. Weather forecasters don't expect to be 100 percent perfect, but it is fun to try.

Getting the Data

Read the following national weather report for July 4, 2006.

Temperature

There are extremely hot temperatures across the United States. It is at least 90 degrees in all parts of the southeast from Virginia to Florida all the way to Texas. Nevada and Arizona are also in the 90s. The rest of the country, including California, is in the 80s, with a few locations in northern Maine in the 70s.

Air Masses and Fronts

A warm front is moving out of the northeast around Massachusetts. A cold air mass that stretches from Michigan through Kansas and into Texas is moving east. These air masses are producing an occluded front in Canada. Behind the cold air mass are lower temperatures and a region of high pressure through North Dakota, South Dakota, and Montana down to Colorado. Near Washington state is a region of low pressure and behind it, a cold air mass.

Precipitation

Rain is moving along the lines of the cold front. More rain is behind the region of high pressure, moving east out of California.

Creating A Weather Map

Use the U.S. Weather Maps and weather symbols to create a map of today's weather for July 4, 2006.

1. Draw locations of fronts using the symbols you learned about in this unit.

2. Use H and L and isobar lines to show high-and low-pressure areas of air.

3. Use green to show areas of precipitation.

Now predict and draw the locations of fronts, Highs and Lows, and precipitation for the next three days. Here are some forecasting tips:

• If there is a lot of water vapor in the air and a cold front is approaching, precipitation is most likely on its way, too.

• A change in air pressure means there will most likely be a change in weather. Falling air pressure generally means rain.

• Rising air pressure generally means clearing skies.

• Air masses and fronts generally move west to east.

Forecasting

As a weather forecaster, you must explain the weather maps to your viewing or reading audience. Write a weather report for the next three days explaining your forecast. Describe changes in pressure, temperature, and precipitation.

July 5, 2006

_____

_____

_____

_____

_____

_____

July 6, 2006

_____

_____

_____

_____

_____

_____

July 7, 2006

_____

_____

_____

_____

_____

_____

Check Your Forecast

When finished, have an adult share the actual forecast and map with you for July 4 to July 7, 2006. How do you rate as a forecaster? What did you predict correctly? What did you predict incorrectly?

_____

_____

_____

_____

What was most challenging about forecasting the weather? How is this similar to the job of a real meteorologist?

_____

_____

_____

Would you rather know the weather each day with 100 percent accuracy, or would you rather be surprised?

_____

_____

_____

Lots of factors influence the weather on a daily basis such as winds, air movement, mountains, large bodies of water, and high elevations. You will learn about these in the next few lessons.

Weather forecasters do not expect to be perfect, but it is fun to test your skills of prediction. You may not have been 100 percent accurate, but you did practice some skills in predicting weather. There are many more things you can do or research to become a better forecaster.

ASSESS

Lesson Assessment: LAB: Working with Weather (*Online*)

Have an adult review your answers to the Build a Barometer and Working with Scientific Data: Weather Forecasting labs and input the results online.

Name _____ Date _____

Build a Barometer

Introduction

Using some simple household materials, you can construct a working barometer. Your reading will not be exact without mercury, but you can get an idea of the rise and fall of air pressure and of the related changes in weather.

Materials

glass jar without lid
large balloon
thick rubber band
drinking straw
masking tape
ruler
toothpick
scissors

Procedure

Build the Barometer

1. Using the scissors, cut the neck off the balloon. Throw the neck of the balloon away.

2. Carefully stretch the large piece of the balloon over the opening of the jar.

3. Use the rubber band to hold the stretched balloon firmly in place over the opening of the jar.

4. Tape the toothpick to the straw so that it is pointing from one end of the straw.

5. Tape the other end of the straw to the center of the balloon. Your barometer is now complete!

Balloon · Straw · Toothpick

Mason Jar

Ruler →

Taking Measurements

6. Find a flat place outside where you can set your barometer for the next 10 days.

7. Hold the ruler vertically on a flat surface, with the "0" at the bottom. Measure the height of the toothpick, in millimeters.

8. Record the data in the data table and write a brief description of today's weather (dry, rainy, windy, etc.).

9. Repeat steps 7 and 8 for the next nine consecutive days. Try to take readings at the same time each day.

Data Table

Day	Time	Height of Toothpick in mm	Current Weather Conditions

Analysis:

Using the graph paper, create a line graph of your data. Along the bottom, write a number for each day. Along the left side, add numbers from 1–25. Place a dot above each day at that day's measurement, and then connect the dots.

Tip: You may trim the graph paper and glue it onto another piece of paper if you need more room or less boxes.

Conclusion

1. Explain how your barometer worked. How was this different from a real barometer?

   _____

   _____

   _____

   _____

2. What relationship did you notice between the height of the toothpick and the current weather conditions at the time of testing?

   _____

   _____

3. If the height of the toothpick was very low, what kind of weather would you expect to experience?

   _____

   _____

Science Club Idea

Communication and working together are important scientific skills. Use your school's message board to find out about other Earth Science students' results from this activity. Or, talk to your teacher to find students in other cities or states and compare your air pressure measurements to theirs.

Name _____   Date _____

U.S. Weather Maps

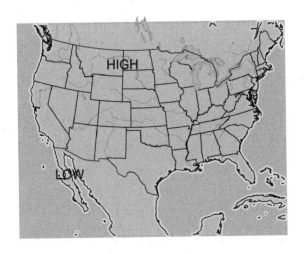

_____

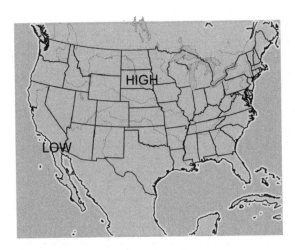

_____

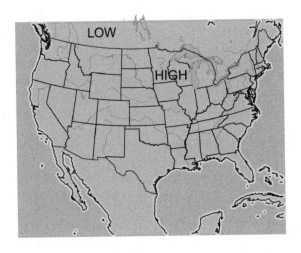

_____

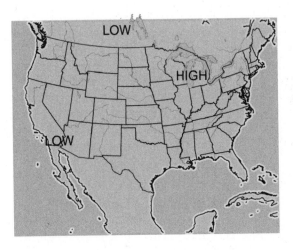

_____

Name   Date

Graph Paper

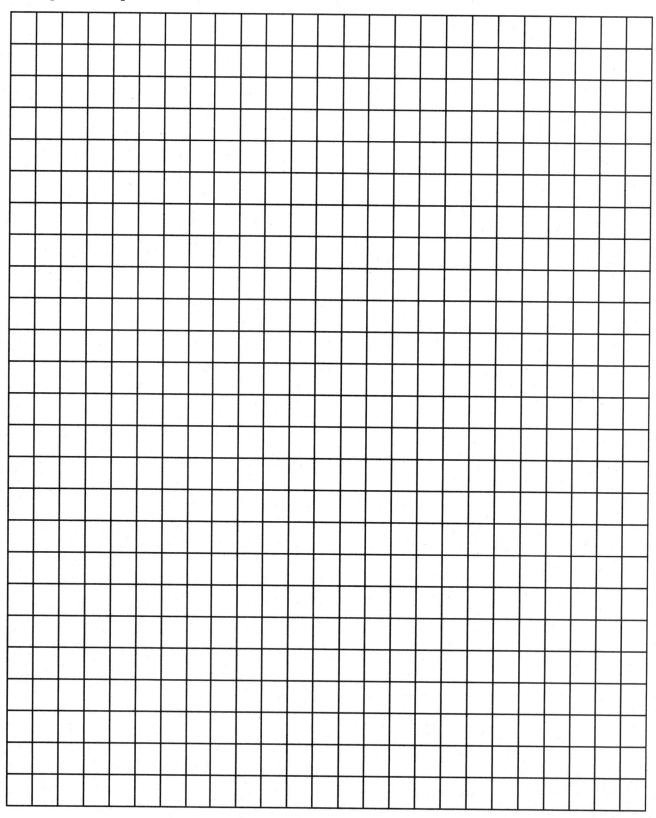

Name _____   Date _____

LAB: Working with Weather Lesson Assessment

1. After completing the procedures in the attached Build a Barometer Lab, complete the Data Table to record your observations.

Day	Time	Height of Toothpick in mm	Current Weather Conditions

2. After completing the procedures in the attached Build a Barometer Lab, use the information in your Data Table to create a line graph showing the changes in air pressure throughout your experiment.

   Along the bottom, write a number for each day. Along the left side, add numbers from 1–25. Place a dot above each day at that day's measurement, and then connect the dots.

3. After completing the procedures in the attached Build a Barometer Lab, explain how your barometer worked. How was this different from a real barometer?

4. After completing the procedures in the attached Build a Barometer Lab, what relationship did you notice between the height of the toothpick and the current weather conditions at the time of testing?

5. After completing the procedures in the attached Build a Barometer Lab, if the height of the toothpick was very low, what kind of weather would you expect to experience?

6. After completing the procedures in the Working with Scientific Data: Weather Forecasting activity in the Student Guide, use the attached U.S. Weather Maps sheet to create a map of today's weather for July 4, 2006. Use the remaining maps to predict and draw the locations of front, Highs and Lows, and precipitation for the next three days.

7. After completing the procedures in the Working with Scientific Data: Weather Forecasting activity in the Student Guide, write a weather report for the next three days explaining the forecast in your weather maps.

8. After completing the procedures in the Working with Scientific Data: Weather Forecasting activity in the Student Guide, explain the challenges associated with predicting weather.

Student Guide
Lesson 10. Optional: Your Choice

Lesson Objectives

- Practice skills and reinforce concepts taught in this course.

PREPARE

Approximate lesson time is 60 minutes.

Student Guide
Lesson 11: Weather and Climate

You may have heard the words "weather" and "climate," but may not have known that there is a difference. The local weather is what determines the climate of an area. The weather can change on a daily basis, but the average weather conditions over the long term are known as an area's climate.

Lesson Objectives

- Define climate as the long-term average of atmospheric conditions for a given region as described by weather observations.
- Contrast weather and climate.
- Describe and locate on a world map the main climate types (polar, temperate, and tropical).
- Explain the influence of latitude on climate conditions and patterns.

PREPARE

Approximate lesson time is 60 minutes.

Materials

For the Student

    📃 Climate Data Chart

    K12 Wall Map

    markers or crayons

    self-sticking notepad

    📃 Climate Around the World

Keywords and Pronunciation

climate : the long-term pattern of weather over time for a particular area, including temperature and precipitation

climate zone : area on earth that has similar temperature, rainfall, snowfall, and sunshine

climatologist (kliy-muh-TAH-luh-jist) : a scientist who studies long-term weather patterns

weather : the day-to-day conditions of an area, including the temperature, wind direction and speed, air pressure, relative humidity, and precipitation

---

LEARN
Activity 1: Weather and Climate *(Online)*

Print out the Climate Data Chart and look over the data provided. As you read through this lesson, follow the directions on-screen to label each city or place from the Climate Data Chart on your U.S. Wall Map.

Activity 2: Climates Around the World (Offline)

Instructions

Take a global view of climate by examining the average yearly temperatures and precipitation in cities around the world. Analyze their locations and decide what factors make their climates different from one another. Use your World Map, previous lessons, and the Internet to record and study the climates of different regions around the globe.

First print Climate Around the World. Then use latitude and longitude to label each city on your map. Next visit the World Climate website to find climate information about your city. Record the average yearly climate information in the chart and answer the questions.

ASSESS

Lesson Assessment: Weather and Climate (Online)

You will complete an offline assessment covering the main objectives of this lesson. Your learning coach will score this assessment.

Name _____   Date _____

Climate Data Chart

City	Temp./Precip.	J	F	M	A	M	J	J	A	S	O	N	D	Average/Total
A Climate: Key West, FL	°C	21	22	23	24	26	28	28	29	29	26	23	21	25.0
	mm	50.8	33.0	33.0	33.0	91.4	106.7	83.8	114.3	170.2	152.4	53.3	53.3	975.2
B Climate: Yuma, AZ	°C	13	15	18	21	24	29	33	35	30	23	17	13	22.6
	mm	10.2	10.2	7.6	2.5	2.5	2.5	5.1	12.7	10.2	7.6	5.1	12.7	88.9
C Climate: Portland, OR	°C	4	6	8	11	14	17	20	20	16	13	8	5	11.8
	mm	154.9	129.5	119.4	71.1	53.0	40.6	12.7	15.2	48.3	81.3	157.5	177.8	1061.3
D Climate: New York, NY	°C	-1	-1	4	10	16	21	24	22	20	13	7	1	11.3
	mm	83.8	83.8	83.8	86.4	61.0	86.4	106.7	106.7	86.4	86.4	86.4	83.8	1041.6
E Climate: Pribilof Islands, AK	°C	-4	-4	-4	-2	2	6	7	9	7	4	1	-2	1.7
	mm	43.2	30.5	30.5	27.9	27.9	30.5	61.0	81.3	86.4	76.2	63.5	50.8	609.7
H Climate: Mt. Wilson, CA, near Pasadena, CA	°C	6	7	7	10	13	20	23	22	20	14	10	7	13.3
	mm	162.6	167.6	152.4	68.6	30.5	5.1	2.5	2.5	1.3	25.4	50.8	111.8	781.1

Name _____ Date _____

Climate Around the World

Use the map on page 3 and the Internet to record and study the climates of different regions around the globe.

1. Use latitude and longitude to label each city on your map.

2. Visit the World Climate website to find climate information about your city.

3. Record the average yearly climate and total yearly precipitation information in the chart.

4. Answer the questions.

City	Average Yearly Temperature in °C	Total Yearly Precipitation in mm
Minsk, Belarus (Former USSR) (53° N, 27° E)		
Shanghai, China (31° N, 121° E)		
Addis Ababa, Ethiopia (8° N, 38° E)		
Helsinki, Finland (60° N, 24° E)		
Banff, Canada (51° N, 115° W)		
Kuala Lumpur, Malaysia (3° N 101° E)	26.5	2393.6
Buenos Aires, Argentina (34° S, 58° W)		
Jakarta, Indonesia (6° S, 106° E)		

Questions

1. What factor contributes most to the warm climate of Kuala Lumpur?

    _____

2. Banff and Minsk are located at similar latitudes. What could account for Banff's average yearly temperature being lower than Minsk's?

    _____

    _____

3. Which city's climate is most similar to Jakarta; Addis Ababa or Kuala Lumpur? Explain your answer.

    _____

    _____

    _____

4. Shanghai and Buenos Aires are located thousands of miles apart and in different hemispheres. Yet their climates are similar. What reasoning could explain this?

    _____

    _____

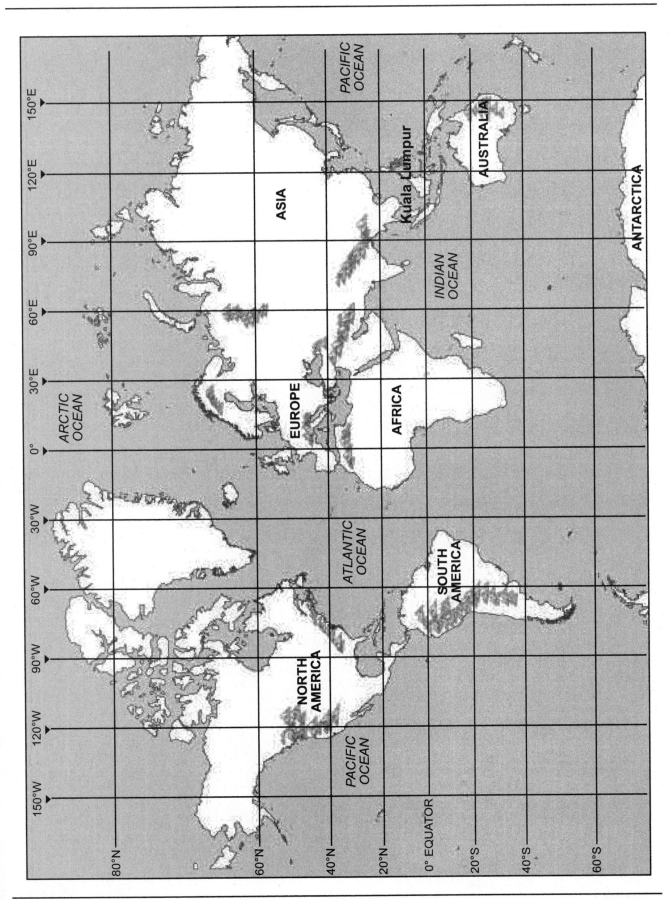

Name _____   Date _____

Weather and Climate Lesson Assessment

Read each question carefully and then answer on the lines provided.

10 pts.

1. Explain the difference between weather and climate.

    _____

    _____

    _____

9 pts.

2. Describe the three major climate types: polar, temperate, and tropical.

    _____

    _____

    _____

    _____

5 pts.

3. How does average temperature change as latitude decreases from the poles to the equator? Why?

    _____

    _____

    _____

Study the map on page 3.

5 pts.

4. Name a city that most likely has a tropical climate.

    _____

    _____

Name _____   Date _____

5 pts.

5.   Name a city that most likely has a temperate climate.

_____

5 pts.

6.   Name a city that most likely has a polar climate.

_____

Name _____   Date _____

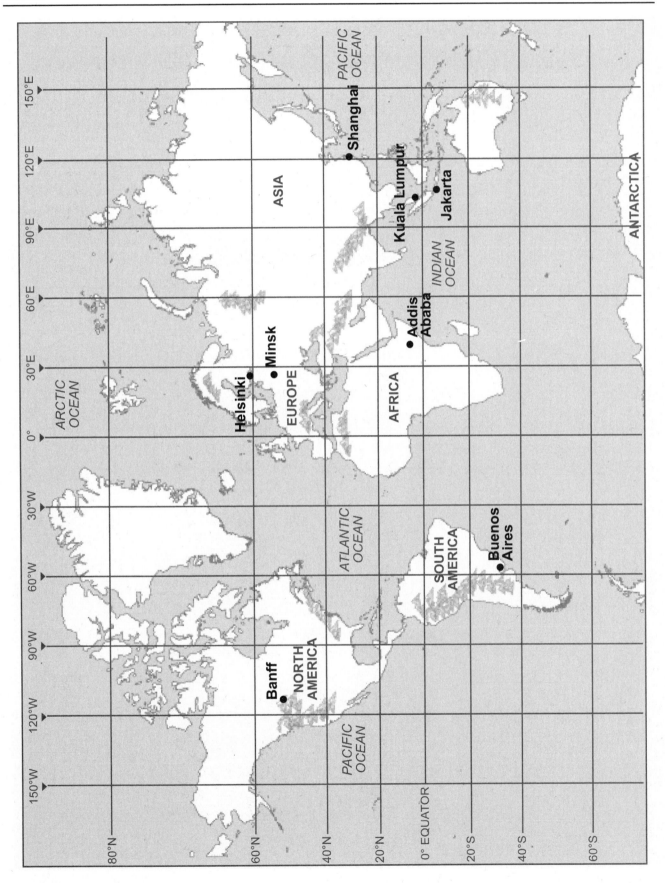

Student Guide
Lesson 12: Factors Affecting Climate

As you learn more and more about earth, you may start to feel appreciation for its extraordinary landscapes and surprising variety. Though you may live in a climate that is hot and dry, just one plane ride can take you where you can find yourself surrounded by snow-covered mountains or cooled by coastal breezes. Earth is an awesome place.

Lesson Objectives

- Analyze how the following factors affect climate: land elevation, geographic location, ocean currents, and proximity to bodies of water.
- Explain how mountain ranges and other major geographical features influence climate patterns.
- Recognize the major influences of solar energy on wind, ocean currents, and the water cycle.

PREPARE

Approximate lesson time is 60 minutes.

Materials

For the Student
- Home Sweet Biome
- North America Map

markers or crayons

Keywords and Pronunciation

conduction : the transfer of heat between two adjoining objects, caused by a temperature difference between the objects

convection (kuhn-VEK-shuhn) : the transfer of heat by the circulation or movement of the heated parts of a liquid or gas

radiation : the process in which energy is emitted by one body, transmitted through an intervening medium or space, and absorbed by another body

LEARN
Activity 1: Factors Affecting Climate *(Online)*

Activity 2: Home Sweet Biome *(Offline)*
Interest Inventory

Finding a new place to live in is no easy task, but we will help you through it. Here's how.

Step 1. Take an inventory of your likes and dislikes in weather, in recreation, and in lifestyle.

Step 2. Discover North America's biomes, their characteristic climates, terrain, and weather patterns.

Step 3. Use your research to decide on a biome that best fits your preferences.

Step 4. Choose a spot to live in and tell why you picked it.

Step 5. Describe your new life and the changes you've made for the folks "back home."

Step 1: Interest Inventory

Complete the following questions to determine what you are looking for in your new home.

1. My favorite season is _____.
2. True or false: I'd rather swim at the beach than take a walk in the woods. _____
3. True or false: I prefer water activities to snow activities. _____
4. True or false: I'd rather be too cold than too hot. _____
5. True or false: I love the rain. _____
6. When it snows, I feel _____.
    a. excited
    b. miserable
    c. cold
    d. ready to go outside
7. I prefer_____.
    a. trees that change color in the fall
    b. leafy green trees that never lose their leaves
    c. tall conifers that reach for the sky and provide shade
    d. wide open plains and big skies
8. If I'm hiking, I prefer_____.
    a. long, flat walks
    b. lots of hills
    c. walks by streams
    d. walks along the seashore
9. The kind of work I would like to do can be done_____.
    a. in any climate.
    b. only in cold climates.
    c. only in warm climates.
    d. only in temperate climates.
10. If my family were planning a vacation, we would probably go to_____.
11. If I drew my favorite landscape, the colors I would need most are _____, _____ and _____.

Activity 3: Home Sweet Biome *(Online)*

ASSESS

Lesson Assessment: Factors Affecting Climate *(Online)*

You will complete an online assessment covering the main objectives of this lesson. Your assessment will be scored by the computer.

Name _____   Date _____

Home Sweet Biome

Step 2: Researching Biomes

Now that your interest inventory is complete, you can start to research different areas to find a place that meets your wants and needs. North America can be divided into seven areas separated by the climate and plant and animal life in them. These seven areas are called biomes.

Using multimedia resources, you will research six biomes (unless you plan to live underwater in the seventh biome, the ocean) and complete the data chart and answer the questions below. The websites below are a good starting point but you may also use books or the Grolier's Online Encyclopedia found in Unit Resources.

Refer to the lesson for links to each website.

- Biome Basics
- World Biomes
- What's it Like Where You Live?

BIOME	CLIMATE	TERRAIN or LAND PATTERN	WEATHER PATTERNS
Tundra			
Grasslands			
Desert			
Taiga			
Rain forest			
Temperate forest			

Name _____   Date _____

1. Which resource provided you with the most information? Write the title and provide the link if it is a website.

    _____

    _____

2. Define the term *biome*.

    _____

    _____

    _____

3. What effect does the terrain of a biome have on its climate and weather?

    _____

    _____

4. On the map of North America, use colored pencils or crayons to color the boundaries of each biome. Make a key.

    _____

    _____

    _____

    _____

    _____

    _____

Step 3 and 4: Where do you want to live?

You will need the answers to the interest inventory and your biome research to complete this section.

5. Which biome contains the climate you prefer?

    _____

6. Why did you choose this biome?

    _____

    _____

    _____

Name _____   Date _____

7.   How would your life be different in this biome?

_____

_____

Step 5: Tell the folks back home

8.   Tell your family and friends back home about your new home! Draw a picture of your biome.
     Write a postcard-sized note about why you love your new home!

STAMP

Name _____ Date _____

North America Map

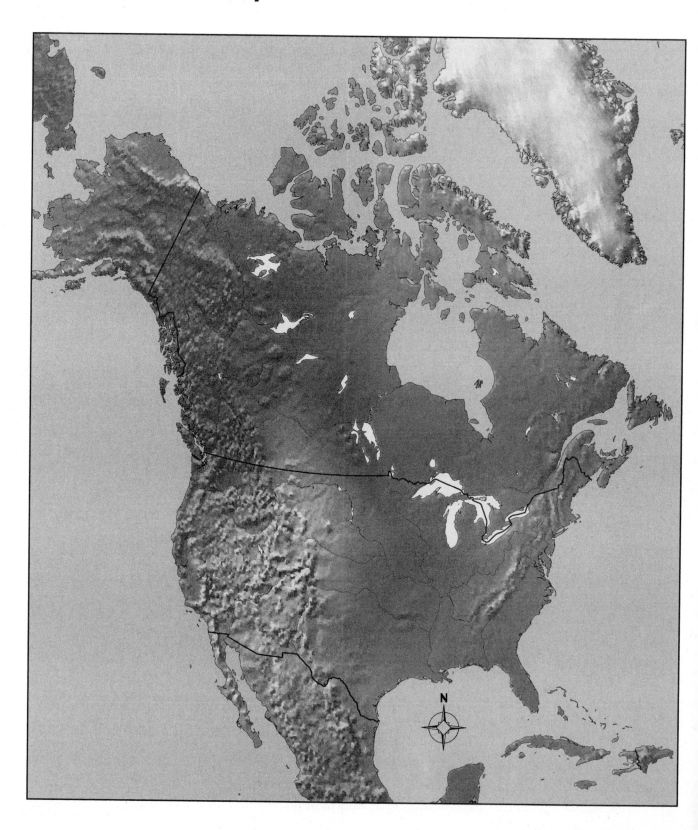

Student Guide
Lesson 13: Lab: Global Warming

What is Global Warming?

Global warming is a trend observed by climatologists and other scientists showing that the average temperature of the earth's atmosphere is increasing. Are humans responsible for this global warming? Some scientists believe that global warming may be creating harmful changes in the earth's atmosphere resulting in an abnormal greenhouse effect that may be changing our weather patterns and possibly melting the world's glaciers.

In this lesson, we will examine the role of carbon dioxide as a greenhouse gas and look at ways we might help stop global warming.

Lesson Objectives

- Explain how the greenhouse effect and the amount of carbon dioxide in the atmosphere are thought to be connected to global warming.
- Describe two possible results of global warming.
- Define global warming as an increase in the average atmospheric temperature.

PREPARE

Approximate lesson time is 60 minutes.

Materials

For the Student

🖳 Understanding Global Warming

Science Notebook

paper

pencil, colored

Optional

glue or tape

newspaper - or magazines

scissors

Keywords and Pronunciation

global warming : an increase in the average temperature of the atmosphere surrounding the earth that is capable of causing a change in climate

greenhouse effect : the process in which the absorption of short wave radiation by the atmosphere heats up a planet

greenhouse gases : atmospheric gases that contribute to the greenhouse effect that include water vapor, nitrous oxide, methane, and carbon dioxide, which is the most abundant

---

LEARN
Activity 1: LAB: Global Warming *(Online)*

Activity 2: Understanding Greenhouse Gases and Global Warming *(Offline)*

Visit the websites listed below and review the information provided. While you are reading over the information, search for the words listed in the word bank.

U.S. EPA - Greenhouse Gas Emissions

http://www.epa.gov/climatechange/emissions/index.html

U.S. EPA - EPA Kid's Greenhouse Effect

http://www.epa.gov/climatechange/kids/greenhouse.html

PBS - PBS NOVA Greenhouse Green Planet

http://www.pbs.org/wgbh/nova/ice/greenhouse.html

PBS - PBS NOVA The Big Chill

http://www.pbs.org/wgbh/nova/ice/chill.html

ASSESS

Lesson Assessment: Lab: Global Warming (*Online*)

Have an adult review your answers to the Understanding Global Warming lab and input the results online.

Name _____   Date _____

Understanding Global Warming

Materials

Science Notebook
paper
colored pencils
scissors
tape
glue

Purpose

The scientific community has been tracking the changes in climate and weather patterns for many years now. Your student has learned that there may be a possible link between human activity and an increase in global temperature and this could result in some unpleasant effects on the earth's atmosphere. The greenhouse effect has a helpful effect on our atmosphere that contributes to life on earth. In this lab, your student will visit some websites to investigate more about what the scientists are learning. Your student will create a concept map to help summarize the ideas presented in this lesson.

Review of the Concept Map

A sample concept map and word bank is provided to help you evaluate your student's work. However, your student's diagram may look quite different from the one provided. In this laboratory, your student should try to be creative and think of as many ways as possible to show the relationships among the ideas presented.

Word Bank

burning fossil fuels	deforestation	car exhaust
solar energy	decaying organic material	cement production
end of Ice Age	helps plants grow	human exhalation
burning coal	keeps earth warm	polar ice caps melting
oceans rising		

Procedure

Visit the websites listed below and review the information provided. While you are reading over the information, search for the words listed in the word bank.

EPA, Climate Change - Greenhouse Gas Emissions: http://www.epa.gov/climatechange/emissions/index.html

EPA Kids Site, Greenhouse Effect: http://epa.gov/climatechange/kids/basics/today/greenhouse-effect.html

Nova Online, Greenhouse - Green Planet: http://www.pbs.org/wgbh/nova/ice/greenhouse.html

What Triggers Ice Ages?

http://www.pbs.org/wgbh/nova/earth/cause-ice-age.html

Steps

1. List under the box Man-Made Sources some examples of how CO_2 may be produced by human activities; one answer could be car emissions. After you have finished the first step, expand your map by adding boxes to show the possible ways that the earth's atmosphere could be hurt by global warming.

2. List under the box Natural Sources some ways that CO_2 is produced naturally; one example might be volcanic activity. When you have finished the first step, expand your map by adding boxes to show the possible ways in which greenhouse gases help the earth's atmosphere.

3. Relax and visualize the information in your head. To make this concept map more exciting, you can cut out pictures from newspapers or magazines showing examples of how CO_2 is made. Or you may want to draw examples of the things you are discovering.

4. Gather paper, markers, and a ruler and some shapes to trace (optional).

5. You should try sketching the diagram in pencil first.

6. You might need to draw more than one map, or think of ways to connect smaller maps to show all of the information. Be creative!

7. Use colors or shapes to show differences between main ideas and supporting details.

8. Check to see that your map is clear and makes sense to you. If not, revise it!

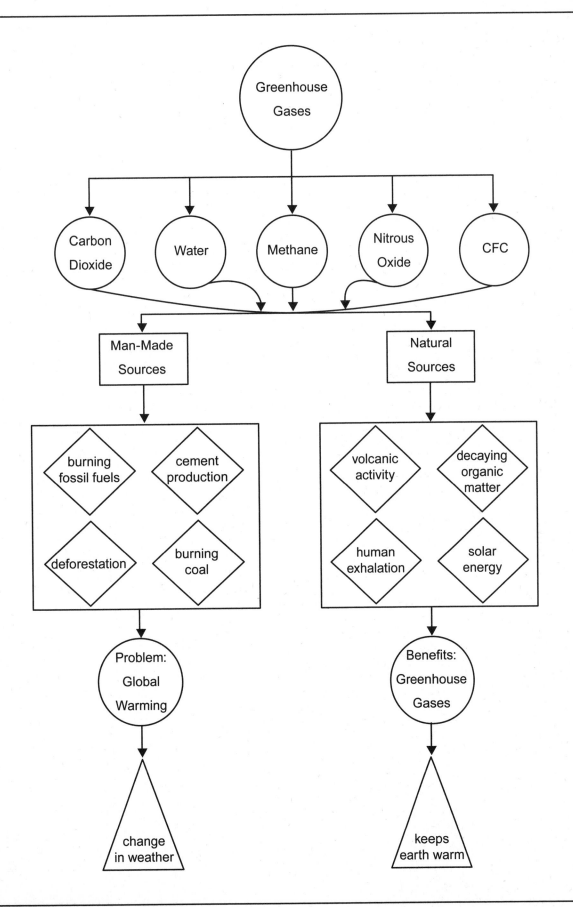

Use the concept map you prepared to help you answer the following questions.

1. Describe at least two things that we can do today to help protect the earth and reduce levels of CO_2.

    _____

    _____

2. Briefly explain how greenhouse gases, carbon dioxide in particular, can absorb and radiate heat inside the earth's atmosphere thereby contributing to the greenhouse effect.

    _____

    _____

    _____

    _____

    _____

3. Read What Triggers Ice Ages?. Briefly describe what you think the world would be like if the amount of greenhouse gases in the atmosphere were reduced to levels like those during the Ice Age.

    _____

    _____

    _____

    _____

Name _____   Date _____

LAB: Global Warming Lesson Assessment

1. Follow the procedures in the Understanding Global Warming lab to create a Concept Map. Use the Concept Map to describe at least two things that we can do today to help protect the earth and reduce levels of CO_2.

2. Follow the procedures in the Understanding Global Warming lab to create a Concept Map. Use the Concept Map to briefly explain how greenhouse gases, carbon dioxide in particular, can absorb and radiate heat inside the earth's atmosphere thereby contributing to the greenhouse effect.

3. Follow the procedures in the attached Understanding Global Warming lab and read The Big Chill from the PBS-NOVA website. Briefly describe what you think the world would be like if the amount of greenhouse gases in the atmosphere were reduced to levels like those during the Ice Age.

Student Guide
Lesson 14: Unit Review

"How's the weather?" used to be a simple question, but now you know that several factors determine weather. You learned about humidity in the air, and about how air masses move to create the weather, winds, climate, and the cycles of energy and water.

Let's review the major concepts before your unit assessment.

Lesson Objectives

- Name and describe the properties of the four main types of air masses that influence weather in North America, locate them on a map, and describe their typical influence on weather.
- Compare the properties of low- and high-pressure areas in terms of air density, pressure, humidity, air motion, and types of associated weather.
- Describe the three mechanisms of heat energy transfer to and among the land, ocean, and air.
- Explain how uneven heating of the earth and the Coriolis effect result in the earth's prevailing winds.
- Explain how large lakes, mountains, and surface ocean currents such as the Gulf Stream can influence climate.
- Explain the main energy transfers in the earth system, explain the greenhouse effect, and recognize that relative constancy of the earth's climates requires that the amount of energy received from the sun roughly equals the amount reflected and radiated from earth into space.
- Name and locate on a world map the three main climate zones (polar, temperate, and tropical) and explain variation in climate in terms of intensity of solar energy, wind, landforms, and ocean currents.
- Describe how air masses interact at cold, warm, stationary, and occluded fronts and describe the clouds and weather they may produce.

PREPARE

Approximate lesson time is 60 minutes.

Materials

For the Student

📖 Weather and Climate Review

LEARN
Activity 1: Air, Weather, and Climate *(Online)*

Activity 2: Weather and Climate Unit Review *(Online)*

Name _____   Date _____

Review

Directions

Read each question carefully and place your answers in the spaces provided. Have the teacher review your work. When you are finished, place your review in your Science Notebook.

1. Explain the atmospheric process that creates the greenhouse effect.

    _____

    _____

    _____

2. Explain why air moves from areas of high pressure to areas of low pressure.

    _____

    _____

    _____

    _____

3. Think about how climate and weather relate to the four spheres of the earth's system. An example would be that land and water heat and cool at different rates, creating coastal winds.

    _____

    _____

    _____

4. Write down some of your own examples of how the spheres relate to climate and weather.

    _____

    _____

    _____

5. Complete the table by deciding which climate type is correct for the region. Some answers are already given in the table.

Air Mass	Temperature (Is it Warm or Cold?)	Humidity (Is it Humid or Dry?)	Air Pressure (Is it High or Low?)
Maritime Polar	Cold		
Maritime Tropical			
Continental Polar		Dry	
Continental Tropical			High
Arctic			

Student Guide
Lesson 15: Unit Assessment

It is important to have a clear understanding of daily weather and the earth's climate. Climate and weather affect everyone—whether you aspire to become a meteorologist, or if you simply need to know the weather in order to plan your daily activities.

Take the Unit Assessment to determine how much you have learned about weather and the earth's climate.

Lesson Objectives

- Name and describe the properties of the four main types of air masses that influence weather in North America, locate them on a map, and describe their typical influence on weather.
- Compare the properties of low- and high-pressure areas in terms of air density, pressure, humidity, air motion, and types of associated weather.
- Describe the three mechanisms of heat energy transfer to and among the land, ocean, and air.
- Explain how uneven heating of the earth and the Coriolis effect result in the earth's prevailing winds.
- Explain how large lakes, mountains, and surface ocean currents such as the Gulf Stream can influence climate.
- Explain the main energy transfers in the earth system, explain the greenhouse effect, and recognize that relative constancy of the earth's climates requires that the amount of energy received from the sun roughly equals the amount reflected and radiated from earth into space.
- Name and locate on a world map the three main climate zones (polar, temperate, and tropical) and explain variation in climate in terms of intensity of solar energy, wind, landforms, and ocean currents.
- Describe how air masses interact at cold, warm, stationary, and occluded fronts and describe the clouds and weather they may produce.

PREPARE

Approximate lesson time is 60 minutes.

ASSESS

Unit Assessment: Air, Weather, and Climate, Part 1 (*Online*)

You will complete an online assessment of the main objectives covered so far in this unit. Follow the instructions online. Your assessment will be scored by the computer.

Unit Assessment: Air, Weather, and Climate, Part 2 (*Offline*)

Complete an offline Unit Assessment. Your learning coach will score this part of the Assessment.

Student Guide
Lesson 1: Semester 1 Review

You are almost finished with your first semester of Earth Science. Let's review the key ideas and prepare to take the assessment.

You have gone through a lot of material this semester, so let's get started.

Looking back, do you recall how the ocean surface currents are caused by the winds? Do you remember the difference between weather and climate? Could you describe the different layers and characteristics of the biosphere?

It's time to discover how much you have learned this semester. Get ready to start your journey from the minerals that make up rock all the way to the atmosphere, stopping everywhere in between.

Lesson Objectives

- Explain how sedimentary rocks are formed and identify features that help determine the type of environment in which they formed.
- State the defining characteristics of a mineral.
- Explain how properties of minerals can be used in their identification.
- Explain how metamorphic rocks are formed.
- Describe evidence that supported the theory of continental drift.
- Describe key features of the theory of plate tectonics.
- Recognize and explain methods by which scientists determine the sequence of geological events, life forms present, and environmental conditions in the past geological eras.
- Describe how air masses interact at cold, warm, stationary, and occluded fronts and describe the clouds and weather they may produce.
- Compare the properties of low- and high-pressure areas in terms of air density, pressure, humidity, air motion, and types of associated weather.
- Describe features on maps such as coordinate systems, scales, directional indicators, keys, symbols, and contour lines.
- Describe major agents of mechanical weathering and of chemical weathering, how the agents cause each kind of weathering, and how mechanical weathering and chemical weathering interact to enhance each other's effects.
- Name and locate on a world map the three main climate zones (polar, temperate, and tropical) and explain variation in climate in terms of intensity of solar energy, wind, landforms, and ocean currents.
- Describe the basic components of the earth's physical systems: atmosphere, biosphere, lithosphere, hydrosphere, and magnetosphere.
- Explain latitude and longitude and recognize them as providing a primary coordinate system for reference to places on the earth.
- Describe major types of soil in terms of porosity, permeability, and climates in which they are found.
- Explain how igneous rocks form and recognize how physical properties of an igneous rock reveal its origin.

- Recognize the principle of uniformitarianism and its importance in determining historical events based on geological information.
- Describe the geologic time scale and provide examples of major geological and biological events of each era.
- Recognize that movements in the earth's crust create seismic waves, which scientists study to learn about earth's interior.
- Explain how uneven heating of the earth and the Coriolis effect create the earth's prevailing winds.
- Explain the main energy transfers of the earth's energy budget, explain the greenhouse effect, and recognize that relative constancy of the earth's climates requires that the amount of energy received from the sun equals the amount reflected and radiated from earth into space.

PREPARE

Approximate lesson time is 60 minutes.

Materials

For the Student

🖳 Semester 1 Review

LEARN
Activity 1: Semester 1 Review (Online)

Activity 2: Semester 1 Review (Online)

You have learned a great deal this semester. Print the Semester 1 Review now to do some more questions.

Name _____   Date _____

Semester 1 Review

Introduction

Looking back, do you recall how the ocean surface currents are caused by the winds? Do you remember the difference between weather and climate? Could you describe the different layers and characteristics of the biosphere? It's time to discover how much information you remember about the material you have learned this semester. Work through this review. Read the questions carefully and place your answers in the spaces provided. Have your teacher review your work when you are finished.

The Spheres of Earth

Imagine the earth as a series of spheres, like the layers of an onion.

1.   If you observed the earth from space, which sphere would you see first?

   _____

2.   Which sphere includes the rocks and minerals?

   _____

Maps

3.   Describe the difference between lines of longitude and lines of latitude. Explain why they are useful.

   _____

   _____

   _____

   _____

Maps and Legends

Some smaller maps, such as road maps, have symbols that indicate places of interest. These could be schools, campsites, airports, or a variety of other things. A key, or map legend, tells you what each symbol means. Scales can help you figure out the distance between two places, and a compass rose indicates the four main directions: north, south, east, and west.

4.   In the box on page 2, draw a map of a town. Use your imagination. Include at least three different places of interest, a map legend, a scale, and a compass rose. Don't forget to name your town. Use your map to answer questions 5 and 6.

5.   To show the elevation of different areas, what does your town map need?

   _____

6. Choose a place of interest on your map and imagine that it is located at the highest point in your town. Draw contour lines on your map to show that this area has the highest elevation.

Making Soil

Soil is the product of weathering. Soil gives plants a place to root as well as the water and nutrients they need to survive. Two factors influence the amount of water in a soil: porosity and permeability. Define each term in the spaces provided.

7. Porosity

_____

_____

8. Permeability

_____

_____

9. Soil can be divided into three categories: sand, silt, and clay. Complete the chart below that describes the porosity and permeability of each soil. Choose High, Moderate, or Low.

Characteristics	Sand	Silt	Clay
Porosity			
Permeability			

Rocks

Minerals are not the only substances that are separated into groups. Rocks are classified, too. They are organized into three groups based on how they form: igneous, sedimentary, and metamorphic. Do you remember how each type of rock forms?

10. Igneous

_____

_____

11. Sedimentary

_____

_____

12. Metamorphic

_____

_____

13. Igneous rocks are classified into two different types: extrusive and intrusive. Explain the difference between extrusive and intrusive igneous rocks.

_____

_____

_____

_____

14. Explain how scientists determine age using relative dating and absolute dating methods.

_____

_____

_____

_____

_____

Continental Drift and Plate Tectonics

A map of the earth drawn 200 million years ago would look much different from the world maps we draw today.

15.   How did Wegener describe the world that existed 200 million years ago?

_____

_____

_____

_____

16.   Describe specific findings on earth's seafloor that supported the theory of plate tectonics.

_____

_____

_____

_____

_____

_____

_____

17.   Describe how scientists use seismic data to analyze the earth's interior structure.

_____

_____

_____

_____

18.   Wind is an important aspect of weather. The rotation of the earth causes the Coriolis effect. Explain this phenomenon.

_____

_____

_____

_____

Climate

Climate refers to the weather patterns that characterize a particular region over a long period of time.

19.   How does latitude influence climate?

_____

_____

20. Describe the three climate zones. Name a country or a place located in each climate zone.

_____

_____

_____

_____

_____

21. Describe how and why each of these variables affects climate.

Ocean currents:

_____

_____

Ocean winds:

_____

_____

Mountains:

_____

_____

_____

Energy Budget

Overall, the earth's climates are relatively stable.

22. Why are earth's climates so stable?

_____

_____

_____

23. Carbon dioxide, methane, water vapor, and other gases in the atmosphere absorb light energy, heat up, and radiate this energy toward the surface of the earth. What process does this describe?

_____

_____

_____

_____

24.   The greenhouse effect isn't always bad for the earth. When does the greenhouse effect become problematic?

_____

_____

_____

_____

Student Guide
Lesson 2: Semester 1 Assessment

You have covered many topics already in this semester of Earth Science.

Take the Semester 1 Assessment now to see how much you have learned.

Lesson Objectives

- State the defining characteristics of a mineral.
- Describe evidence that supported the theory of continental drift.
- Describe key features of the theory of plate tectonics.
- Recognize and explain methods by which scientists determine the sequence of geological events, life forms present, and environmental conditions in the past geological eras.
- Compare the properties of low- and high-pressure areas in terms of air density, pressure, humidity, air motion, and types of associated weather.
- Describe features on maps such as coordinate systems, scales, directional indicators, keys, symbols, and contour lines.
- Describe major types of soil in terms of porosity, permeability, and climates in which they are found.
- Describe the geologic time scale and provide examples of major geological and biological events of each era.
- Name and locate on a world map the three main climate zones (polar, temperate, and tropical) and explain variation in climate in terms of intensity of solar energy, wind, landforms, and ocean currents.
- Describe how air masses interact at cold, warm, stationary, and occluded fronts and describe the clouds and weather they may produce.
- Explain latitude and longitude and recognize them as providing a primary coordinate system for reference to places on the earth.
- Explain how uneven heating of the earth and the Coriolis effect create the earth's prevailing winds.
- Explain how metamorphic rocks are formed.
- Explain how sedimentary rocks are formed and identify features that help determine the type of environment in which they formed.
- Describe major agents of mechanical weathering and of chemical weathering, how the agents cause each kind of weathering, and how mechanical weathering and chemical weathering interact to enhance each other's effects.
- Explain how properties of minerals can be used in their identification.
- Describe evidence that supported the theory of continental drift.
- Describe key features of the theory of plate tectonics.
- Explain the main energy transfers in the earth system, explain the greenhouse effect, and recognize that relative constancy of the earth's climates requires that the amount of energy received from the sun roughly equals the amount reflected and radiated from earth into space.
- Describe the basic components of the earth's physical systems: atmosphere, biosphere, lithosphere, hydrosphere, and magnetosphere.

- Explain how igneous rocks form and recognize how physical properties of an igneous rock reveal its origin.
- Recognize the principle of uniformitarianism and its importance in determining historical events based on geological information.

PREPARE

Approximate lesson time is 60 minutes.

ASSESS

Semester Assessment: Semester 1 Assessment, Part 1 (*Online*)

You will complete an assessment covering the main objectives of this semester. This part of the assessment is online. It will be scored by the computer.

Semester Assessment: Semester 1 Assessment, Part 2 (*Offline*)

Complete an offline Semester Assessment. Your learning coach will score this part of the assessment.